SURGEON IN THE JUNGLE WAR

Surgeon in the Jungle War

John A. Baty, OBE, FRCS

With an introduction by
Major General Ambrose Meneces,
CB, CBE, DSO

WILLIAM KIMBER · LONDON

First published in 1979 by
WILLIAM KIMBER & CO. LIMITED
Godolphin House, 22a Queen Anne's Gate,
London, SW1H 9AE

ISBN 07183 0057 2

Typeset by Input Typesetting Ltd,
and printed and bound in Great Britain
by Redwood Burn, Trowbridge and Esher.

Contents

List of Illustrations

Acknowledgements

The author wishes to express his thanks to Major General Ambrose Meneces for his help, advice and encouragement and for his introduction written for this book. A debt is also due to Major George Quayle and to Major John Dickinson for their contributions to Chapters 3 and 17.

Introduction

by

Major General Ambrose Meneces, CB, CBE, DSO.
Late RAMC and Commandant RAM College, Millbank.

Centuries of war taught such surgeons as Pare, Wiseman, Hunter, Larrey and the British surgical teams in Flanders in 1917–1918, that the most important element in the treatment of wounds was the astonishing power of the human body to resist infection and repair injuries. In World War 1 such surgical procedures as removal of dead and severely damaged tissues, delay in primary suture, immobilisation of limbs in split plaster casts and the exteriorisation of wounds of the large bowel, effected striking reductions in mortality and in the period of recovery. In World War 2, the use of sulphonamides, antibiotics, transfusion, forward surgery, skilled anaesthesia, air transport of casualties and rehabilitation reduced mortality and period of convalescence still further.

But time, place and circumstances require variations in applying surgical skills and practice. In 1943–44, war in Burma against the Japanese was fought over a seven-hundred-mile front (from China to the Bay of Bengal), with jungle-clad precipitous hills, no railways, no roads, merely a few jungle tracks washed away by monsoon rains. Two hundred miles separated the road, railway and river systems of India and Burma. The southern section of the Burma front lay in the Arakan Yomas, razor-edged hill ridges covered to the summit with tight packed foliage through which combat troops, stretcher bearers and mules carrying supplies had to scramble. The few Arakan coastal roads encountered numerous *chaungs*, tidal creeks laced with mangrove swamps running inland from the sea. Apart from enemy action, the heat, thirst, dust, insects, malaria, dysentery, skin diseases and scrub typhus caused many casualties. In 1943, for every soldier evacuated with wounds, one hundred and twenty were evacuated through disease.

In December 1942, the 14th Division commenced a ninety mile advance through the Arakan to re-capture Akyab. From January to March 1943, three assaults by the division at Donbaik near Akyab, were repulsed by the Japanese. Fierce enemy counter attacks on 5th April 1943 caused the abandonment of Maungdaw and Buthidaung and a redeployment with an outpost position at Bawli Bazar. From November 1943, General Sir Philip Christison and XV Corps commenced a counter-offensive and in February 1944 inflicted at Ngakyedauk, a decisive defeat upon the Japanese who withdrew leaving five thousand dead and many more scattered in the jungle. XV Corps continued its advance by assault landings from the sea and the capture of Akyab, Ramree and Letpan provided air bases for the supply of Fourteenth Army during its advance from the north. On 3rd May 1945, XV Corps re-entered Rangoon from the sea.

From May 1943, Major John Baty and his colleagues of No 7 Indian Mobile Surgical Unit were immersed in the maelstrom of the war in Burma. Owing to the initial absence of air transport, casualties had to be evacuated hundreds of miles by jungle paths, *sampans*, road, rail and steamer to India. To provide life-saving surgery in the combat zone, forward surgical teams performed operations within a few hours of a soldier being wounded. Amidst the confusion of the jungle battle, the surgeon had to make a correct assessment, decide quickly and act confidently. From this book it is possible to glean the courage, patient endurance and professional skills which the author and his colleagues displayed in providing surgical cover in the combat zone. It shows how surgical skills and success can be maintained under the most trying circumstances.

AMBROSE MENECES.

Author's Preface

An occasion arose for me to explore the dusty loft above my garage; under the junk I came across the old tin trunk which had lain undisturbed since the war. Beneath mildewed uniforms, I found a collection of surgical records, operation notes, old letters, snapshots, sketches and diaries for 1943–44. My first inclination was to burn the lot, but, after spending several hours browsing and reviving memories of the past, I felt that it would not be out of place to make use of these records to present a picture centred on No 7 Indian Mobile Surgical Unit and of the part it played during the war in Burma.

Of all the mobile units in Burma, No 7 had the distinction of being the longest serving surgical unit in this theatre of war. In the various military histories of the war in South-East Asia, the intimate details of the fighting are adequately recorded but no more than passing mention is made of the part played by the Medical Services, in particular, the Mobile Surgical Units. The combination of climate, jungle, diseases and the Japanese loaded the dice against the wounded and against those whose efforts were directed towards overcoming the difficulties. It is hoped that this true story will fill a gap in the medical history covering this period and at the same time recall episodes which, on occasions, did something to lighten the darkness of those grim years.

CHAPTER ONE

Towards the Rising Sun

I sat under the shade of a creeper-draped *neem* tree and contemplated the situation in which I now found myself. Before me, a rust red track shimmered in the heat, and along it, at irregular intervals, rolled clouds of orange dust which partially concealed convoys of Allied forces, in full retreat from the Arakan front towards the comparative safety of the Indian frontier some thirty miles to the north. The only individuals making any attempt to move in the opposite direction were my driver, his mate and myself, and we had been advancing somewhat erratically until our truck had broken down.

The stream of north-bound traffic became sporadic, eventually all activity along the road ceased. No one had given the least attention to our plight and after the last truck had roared past, the uncanny silence was broken by the resumption of the chorus from the crickets in the tree. Across the track the crested plumes of the bamboo were motionless above the tall elephant grass and behind lay the foetid thickness of the jungle, heavy and full of menace, for this was May 1943. My orders had been to take over the command of No 7 Indian Mobile Surgical Unit last heard of in Maungdaw, Burma and now there seemed to be no alternative but to sweat it out until either our truck could be started or until some south-bound vehicle appeared. I was fully aware that the sudden arrival of a Japanese patrol would surely have brought my career to an abrupt end.

So, in an effort to take my mind off this uncomfortable situation, I let my thoughts range back over the events of the past eighteen months, events which led me, a British surgeon, to the verge of a dirt-track in the hostile Burmese jungle.

Early in 1942, the administrative wheels had been set in motion for the formation of mobile surgical units to work in Burma. Although at this time No 7 Indian Mobile Surgical Unit was no more than a memorandum on some desk in New Delhi, the course of events which led to my joining it were already under way. At the beginning of the war, I had been instructed to continue my work as a surgeon on the staff of the Rotherham General Hospital which was made ready to cope with the expected air-raid casualties. First-aid lectures were given to all those likely to be involved and training exercises were arranged for hospital personnel, for ambulance men and for recruits to the fire service. In the complete blackout, 'incidents' were staged after which the large out-patient hall of the hospital would be overflowing with stretchers on which reclined volunteers wearing labels to indicate the nature of their supposed wounds. All varieties of splints and bandages smothered the 'victims' many of whom had 'M' or 'T' inscribed in iodine on their foreheads to indicate that supposedly morphine had been given or a tourniquet had been applied. (I cannot recollect ever having seen any casualty in Burma so marked and one encountered a number of instances in which morphia and tourniquet problems might have been avoided if this practice had been seriously adopted.)

After a general inspection of the first-aid measures which had been used, there would be a full discussion over mugs of tea; then the 'wounded' and the first-aiders would grope their ways back home. The pride of the service was a fully equipped old ambulance termed the 'Mobile Unit'; it was based at the hospital ready to be manned for a dash out to incidents so that emergency surgery could be carried out on the spot but on the only occasion the mobile unit was called to an 'incident', it got lost in the blackout; the 'casualties' got tired of waiting and cleared off to the nearest pub.

Fortunately for Rotherham, there was never an occasion for the emergency services to be brought into full operation. Incendiary and high-explosive bombs were dropped sporadically but very little damage was caused. Only once during an air-raid was it considered advisable to transfer patients from the wards to the basements. A couple of miners immobilised in traction for broken thighs and a woman whose rectum had been excised the previous day were not fit enough to be moved; throughout the night they cheerfully tolerated the temporary isolation in their respective wards, on the roofs of which rattled the shrapnel from the anti-aircraft guns.

The general public seemed to flourish on war-time restrictions, blackout, coupons and ration books. Most families had at least one of their number in the services or engaged on part-time voluntary work, and at this period there was a very noticeable drop in the number of patients who sought treatment for psychological disorders. The large steel works between Rotherham and Sheffield poured out their smoke and fumes into the atmosphere to create a smog which confused the German bombers as well as those of us who had to find our ways about on the ground. During the winter, a combination of smog, masked headlamps, ice and snow made night calls an experience nearly as worrying as my later blackout journeys along the jungle trails of Burma. The Special Constables and Home Guard enjoyed their new responsibilities. Some may have been a little over-zealous, as on one winter's night when a woman in labour was held up at a road block. After the taxi had been brought to a halt, a home guardsman, armed with a broomstick handle in lieu of a weapon, approached the cab:

'Hello, Mrs Smitheman. You're out late. I'll need to have a look at your identity card.'

'So sorry, Mr Tuke, I forgot to bring it with me as I had to leave home in a hurry.'

'My instructions are that no one must pass without showing an identity card so you'll have to go back and get it.'

'There's no time. I'm in labour already.'

'Can't be helped but I've got my job to do. There's a war on you know.'

'Oh, for Gawd's sake, Mr Tuke! I don't want to have the baby in this taxi. I can't go back now. The pains are coming on fast.'

Eventually a return of contractions forced Mr Tuke to disobey his orders and let her through. In the labour ward shortly afterwards, between pains, the patient found strength loudly to curse Hitler and the Home Guard in general and Mr Tuke in particular.

Eventually the call came for me to join the RAMC in February 1942 when, feeling a little self-conscious in my new uniform and sporting the two pips of a lieutenant, I travelled to Becket's Park, Leeds, for a fortnight's preliminary training course. During this time, I was initiated into the proper use of army forms and told how to classify soldiers into their correct medical categories. I found out about the functions of base hospitals, casualty clearing stations, main and advanced dressing stations but have no recollection of hearing any mention of 'mobile surgical units'. Quite an appreciable part of the time was spent on learning to drill, how to salute and what to do with a swagger stick. Instructions were given on the uses of the compass and its application in map references. To bring home the importance of this subject, a special exercise was arranged in the country north of the city; on a black rainy night, transport dropped off small groups of officers at scattered points, the map references being given. We were required within a few hours to get to another map reference some five miles away, where trucks and hot drinks would be waiting. Most groups found the rendezvous with time to spare but those who got lost were confronted with a long, wearisome, wet walk back to camp. Later, when journeying along jungle trails in Arakan, I fully appreciated that a mistake in map-reading there would have consequences far more serious than a walk back to Leeds.

Barely settled into army life, all personnel were required to indicate if they were anxious to have their names put forward for early overseas service. I considered that it was best not to volunteer for anything, so that should misfortune befall at least I could not blame it on myself. Events were to prove however, that those who did volunteer were unlikely to have left the UK more quickly than I did.

Soon a week was spent at Mychett, near Aldershot, where, whilst we recovered from our various inoculations, experts delivered hygiene lectures and arranged demonstrations. A stout short-sighted major tried to instill some humour into his talk on tropical diseases; in hindsight, it seems likely that he had never been abroad. He did, however, manage to raise the odd nervous laugh from his audience but after the lecture, most men were hoping for a posting to Arctic regions rather than east of Suez. On the gorse-covered common surrounding the camp, small groups were instructed in the arts of tent erection, latrine construction and cook-house organisation in the field. From amongst the large amount of information provided, one item came in particularly useful in 1943 when the mobile unit's large primus stove broke down at a most inopportune time. Until a replacement could be obtained, some alternative had to be found in order to continue with pressure sterilisation; after much head-scratching and experimentation, eventually it was found possible to assemble an oil-water flash stove which worked just as well as the one demonstrated at Mychett.

My first posting was as surgical specialist to the Military Hospital at Tidworth, which was a busy centre for all types of medical work. At the twice-weekly clinics, I had to winkle out those soldiers who had disabilities which required attention before overseas service could be permitted. Men with hernias or those with painful feet made up the bulk of the outpatients. Occasionally bed-wetters attended and these had to be admitted for cystoscopy (examination of the interior of the bladder) which invariably proved negative; this somewhat unsocial complaint gave them the ticket for an early return to civilian life. I soon encountered the attitude of the regular RAMC quartermaster who considered that an instrument was best kept in stores rather than in use. The operating cystoscope is a delicate instrument through which not only can the interior of the bladder be inspected but along it small catheters can be passed up the ureters to the kidneys. One morning, after prolonged lack of success in my efforts to catheterise the ureters, I enquired of the theatre orderly:

'How did my predecessor, Major Hickie, manage with this cystoscope?'

'He could not get it to work either, sir.'

'Well how did he cope with cases like this?'

'Oh, I borrowed the new cystoscope out of the stores.'

'Then why return it to the stores?'

'The QM wanted it back and I thought it would be a good idea to see if you could get the old instrument to work, sir.'

Once I had visited the stores, argued with the man in charge and given my signature in triplicate, a properly functioning instrument was issued for regular use in the theatre.

One gunner was referred to surgical out-patients on account of undescended testicles on both sides. In this congenital condition, the testicles have failed to reach the scrotum and have remained in the groins where they are more susceptible to injury. It is generally accepted that such testicles, after the age of puberty, are no longer capable of producing sperms. To my suggestion that he should be admitted the next week for operation, he had many objections, the final one being that he was getting married. This seemed to be an opportunity to press home the argument for operation:

'Since you intend to get married, it is especially important that you should have the operation as without it, you are unlikely to father any children. I suggest that you postpone the wedding to a later date.'

'No. I can't do that.'

'Why not?'

'Because I'm having to get married.'

Having failed with my arguments, there was no alternative but to mark him in a category as being unsuitable for overseas service. No doubt he congratulated himself on being the exception to the rule. I have always wondered that it never at a later date crossed his mind that there was an alternative explanation!

Tidworth was a centre designated for the repair of recurrent hernias which resulted from the policy of getting soldiers back to full duties within six weeks of their original operation; the bulk of the routine operating lists were made up of cases of this type. Acute appendices and perforated ulcers were the usual emergency admissions but there was one remarkable accident in which a soldier nearly killed himself on a loaf of bread! This man, on leaving the canteen with a loaf under his left arm, had tripped and fallen on his left side. His respirator had swung round into the gap between arm and trunk; the full weight of the fall had driven the rigid canister into the lower left ribs causing severe bleeding into the abdominal cavity. He made a full recovery after removal of a ruptured spleen.

The activities of local troops training with live ammunition provided a steady flow of casualties. The climax came as the result of an unfortunate event on Salisbury Plain, when Hurricane fighters were demonstrating a low level attack on ground targets, before a large gathering of officers, many of whom were of high rank. This show was to have been a rehearsal for the following day when a similar exercise was to be viewed by Winston Churchill (the PM's visit was cancelled). The first two fighters were on target but the third went off course and its machine guns blasted the spectators. Major Philip Wiles, the orthopaedic surgeon, arranged the reception, resuscitation and sorting out of survivors, who were passed on to me in the operating theatre. The first arrival was General Templer, who had escaped with a minor bullet wound of the chin and was more concerned as to how such a tragedy could have occurred. At the time it was suggested that the dust thrown up by the first two planes had obscured the target for the third.

A few months later, in a Durban cinema, I saw a news film which must have escaped the censor and actually included shots of the incident. The commentator in a somewhat jocular tone described this training exercise and remarked that it looked as if the planes were putting the wind up the spectators! He did not mention that there on the screen was a clear record of not only casualties but deaths, actually being inflicted. This disaster on Salisbury Plain gave me a foretaste of a similar accident in Burma, in August 1943, involving another squadron of Hurricanes.

In the May of 1942, I managed to find accommodation in Shipton Bellinger for my wife, Kathie, and four-year-old daughter, Margot. They brought our spaniel, Pedro, with them and the next day I attended Andover station to collect the Scottie, Rip, who had travelled on his own by train from Rotherham. He was delighted to see me and after the fuss had subsided, there was no difficulty in getting him to sit on a cushion over the cross bar of my bicycle with his front paws on the handle bars, whilst I pedalled back to Shipton.

Unfortunately, within a week of Rip's arrival, for me there came the posting order to Alloa, Clackmannanshire, there to join the 80th British General Hospital preparing for service overseas. Lieutenant-Colonel Gilroy Glass who commanded this 200-bedded hospital was in a disgruntled frame of mind at having me thrust upon him as surgical specialist and second in command. My predecessor, a Territorial, had been with the 80th since its formation; he knew all aspects of army hospital administration and was an authority on rules, regulations and documentation. It came as a sad blow to the Colonel to find that his able and experienced right-hand man had been posted to another unit. The cold reception I received from Glass was, however, more than compensated for by meeting the medical specialist, William Wallace, and the pathologist, Maurice Joseph, with whom a life-long friendship was started.

On being told to take immediate embarkation leave, a wire was sent to my wife in Shipton and reached her shortly after breakfast. A hurried packing and every assistance from the O/C Tidworth Hospital, who arranged transport to Andover junction, saw the family on their way by lunchtime. Following a tedious journey with a couple of dogs and an active child, my wife, in an exhausted state reached Rotherham just before midnight and I arrived home a few hours later. After ten days, the farewells had to be said and a parting, which was to last for near on four years, had to be made.

Once again I travelled north but on this occasion, the journey was more complicated because of previous enemy action; York had been bombed during the night and the station roof was still on fire when the train from the south drew in. The main line had been blocked and after much delay from re-routing, I reached Waverley Station, Edinburgh, many hours late. It was still possible to get a connection across the Forth Bridge, but from Dunfermline all trains had long since departed. A visit was paid to the station-master to explain the situation; when it was pointed out to him the importance of re-joining units about to embark, he cut red tape and laid on a special consisting of an engine drawing a single coach in which I, with half a dozen others, completed the journey to Alloa.

A few days later, the Hospital entrained for Gourock and along with many combatant units settled on the SS *Pasteur* which sailed that evening. *Pasteur* was a large French liner which, in view of its reputation for rolling badly in heavy seas, had come to the Clyde to have bilge keels fitted but there was no time for these modifications to be made and within 48 hours of her arrival she was provisioned, loaded and heading out into the Atlantic. It was some weeks later that we sadly missed the bilge keels as, round the Cape of Good Hope, *Pasteur* steadily rolled 15 degrees to each side. In the twilight, whilst the Paps of Jura were still visible in the darkening east, our group of ships was joined by a contingent from Northern Ireland to make up a large convoy escorted by a battle-cruiser and a couple of destroyers.

Aboard the large troopship which occupied the rear of the convoy, we soon settled down to the daily routine of inspections, boat drills and look-out duties. From the surgical aspect, the only incident occurred somewhere in the North Atlantic, when I had to deal with a soldier who was in severe pain from a perforated duodenal ulcer. The ship's captain, on being asked about heaving-to for the operation, pointed out that we were in submarine waters and he could not risk a stop. He added that course was being changed every twenty minutes. With this comforting assurance, we made all ready in the small but well-appointed operating theatre situated low down towards the bow. The patient was under the anaesthetic when the ship made its great lurch and the floor suddenly sloped at a new angle. The operation was satisfactorily completed before the ship again lurched on to a new course. The patient who was a native of South Yorkshire, made a good recovery; he was put ashore at Freetown, our first port of call. After being transferred back to the UK, he kept his promise to call on my wife in Rotherham and so gave her her first news of me.

Following an extensive tour of the North Atlantic, our convoy approached the Gold Coast of West Africa. Here, the appearance of a squadron of Vichy French bombers from Dakar produced a scattering of the ships; there was some ack-ack fire and the medical stations were manned ready for casualties, though none materialised. The remainder of the trip to Sierra Leone was uneventful and the weekend was spent anchored in the estuary at Freetown. No shore leave was permitted but entertainment was provided by a most spectacular tropical thunderstorm.

Our convoy then headed south, crossed the Equator without ceremony, passed St Helena and rolled round the Cape of Good Hope to reach Durban. As *Pasteur* drew alongside the dock, we were greeted by the famous 'Lady in White'. She was a greatly talented professional singer, who, as her war effort, made a point of being on the quayside to welcome the arriving troopships. In a powerful faultless voice, without any accompaniment, she entertained with her selection of popular songs.

After the blackout at home, Durban, fully illuminated presented an impressive sight which, however, was of short duration as at the same time as the arrival of our convoy, enemy submarines had been reported off the coast, so that night Durban, with much confusion, joined the blackout. There was a scramble to catch the last train back to camp. Visibility was nil in our crowded compartment where one drunken Scot, in a broad Glaswegian accent, laid forth his views throughout the whole journey. Loudly, with every other word a curse, he colourfully expressed the opinion that fate had played him a particularly dirty trick. At home, he had just started enjoying a peaceful six months gaol sentence when 'they' shot him out of prison, made him join the army and shipped him overseas before he had time to '–ing well break wind!'

Durban at this time was only just recovering from the effects of the previous convoy, which had unleashed the Australians to create havoc in the city. The resulting restrictions were gradually being relaxed and troops were no longer completely banned from all places of night recreation. During our short stay at Clarewood Transit Camp, some twenty minutes by train from Durban, entertainment was provided by the city's cinemas, hotel bars, restaurants and night clubs. The latter, in particular the Starlight, were a dead loss. Although outside, a tot of brandy could be had for sixpence, in the club, even a jug of orange juice cost 30/-, which seemed a high price to pay for sitting in a dim, airless, humid atmosphere listening to the leader of the band singing about three old ladies locked in a lavatory! Soon a cheaper recreation was sought and found. A few miles south of Clarewood, we could enjoy free surf bathing in the huge pounding breakers on the beaches of Isipingo and Amanzototti.

Gilroy Glass had a cousin who ran a sugar plantation some fifty miles inland from Durban; as a special treat, shortly after our arrival, the 80th BGH was invited to the plantation, where a Zulu war-dance festival was being held. Transport was arranged in trucks used for carrying sugar cane, and the Indian drivers of these vehicles demonstrated their prowess at the wheel by accelerating down long inclines and then violently braking to negotiate narrow bridges in the valleys. During the long sea voyage the majority of the unit had developed a tendency towards constipation, but the

(*Top*) The author and W. D. Wallace at Clarewood Camp.
(*Bottom*) Some of the officers of 80th BGH

War dance festival in Zululand

drive through the Valley of a Thousand Hills certainly reversed this state of affairs!

In the vast tented camp, the only brick structures were the administrative block and the small hospital. I had occasion to visit this hospital when I received a message from the O/C Surgical Division of the 14 BGH, Colonel John Bruce, who had been admitted there with a strained knee. He suggested that I should look him up and so, on several occasions, we had tea together whilst we chatted about Edinburgh and surgery. Thereafter, in India and Burma, I, from time to time, enjoyed the company of John Bruce, who proved to be a good adviser and staunch friend.

Guard duties at the camp were, in part, provided by coloured South African troops who were very proud to be seen on parade sporting their *assegai* and wearing shorts which, for modesty's sake, reached below the knees. Some of these men, however, complained to their officers that they were being treated unfairly when they saw British soldiers in full kit being marched back and forth on the hot dusty parade ground. When they asked why they could not be given this special drill, it was tactfully explained to them that these Cameronians were undergoing punishment for their misdeeds.

Whilst resident in Clarewood camp, one of my duties was to hold clinics and sort out men who, before going further, would need some operation in a Durban hospital. One such soldier attended with a tense groin swelling (an irreduceable femoral hernia) and instructions were given that he should receive surgical attention without delay. Some ten days later, when I was aboard SS *Yoma* out in the Indian Ocean, I was surprised to be asked to examine the same man again, for I had ordered him to remain at Durban until his treatment had been completed. But in order to remain with his unit, he had ignored my recommendations and now was experiencing abdominal pains with vomiting; it was fortunate that his symptoms settled with conservative measures, as surgical facilities aboard were virtually non-existent.

We had left Durban on *Yoma*, an ancient cargo vessel never intended for the transport of passengers, let alone hundreds of troops. As the ship slowly moved towards the open ocean, several men, would-be deserters, risked the sharks by going overboard and swimming back to the jetty which they safely reached to be welcomed into the arms of the military police. In our trip out from the Clyde, we had been accommodated on one of the world's largest liners which was the pride of the convoy. *Yoma*, which took us from South Africa, was little more than an ill-favoured tramp which soon showed that she could not keep up with the rest of the convoy. Each morning on waking, we could see on the horizon the smoke from distant vessels. Full steam would then be put on and by dusk *Yoma* would nearly have caught up; during the night it was found that speed could not be maintained and by dawn we were on our own again. At first the single escorting frigate would bustle back to allow instructions to be shouted across to our skipper but after a few days these return visits were discontinued.

It was while crossing the Indian Ocean that I was given a foretaste of surgery under adverse conditions. As a result of a fall from his hammock, a man sustained a severe laceration of the forearm and elbow; operation was required but all our surgical equipment was inaccessible, stowed at the bottom of the ship's hold under tons of other supplies. So first we had to have a wooden table moved into the afterdeck cabin and then material was cut up to make swabs which were boiled in a billycan; from the chiropodist it was possible to borrow one pair of artery forceps and some scissors; I provided needle and thread from my 'hussif', and the ship's captain managed to find a bottle of chloroform. Thus the operation was carried out, near the Equator, in the still heat of the doldrums. All concerned, wearing nothing but underpants, lost many pints of sweat. In spite of the difficulties, there were no complications and by the time Bombay was reached the wound had healed without any infection.

A second-in-command of the 80th BGH, I was privileged to share a cabin with Gilroy Glass, whose moods were somewhat variable and unpredictable; he did however teach me two-handed patience, a game he always won. Later, in Burma, this card game helped the passage of many weary hours. During the daytime, even the slow progress of *Yoma* created some slight movement of air to bring a little relief to the equatorial heat. At night, strict blackout meant closed portholes; this, combined with the antiquated ventilation system, resulted in a Turkish bath existence below deck. As usual on board ship, soft drinks and beer were expensive and in short supply but there was no lack of cheap gin, whisky and rum. From time to time, cocktail parties were given and then perhaps half a dozen of officers would crowd into the host's cabin and there, combining alcohol with a great deal of talk, attempt to forget the heat. At one such party, since there was a mug short, a visit was paid to the adjoining cabin where Captain Maurice Joseph had settled for the night. Without disturbing his snores, a bakelite mug was borrowed in which a generous gin and lime was handed to general duties officer, Captain Colin MacDonald. As the first swig was taken, Colin was somewhat shaken when a dental plate bearing a couple of teeth rattled into his mouth. It was fortunate that the denture had not been immersed in any scouring fluid, otherwise the lining of his gullet might have been burnt off.

In the tropical seas at night, we frequently saw the illuminated wake made by the ship; on one such night, when the same Colin was refreshing himself in a sea-water bath, he called out for me to come into the bathroom in order to view his body which, in the gloom, was seen to be covered with luminous patches. We removed some of these patches and found they were small, amoeba-like creatures composed of clear jelly in the centre of which were several brown spots. When shaken up in water these brown spots developed a fluorescence which gradually subsided once the agitation was discontinued. Our research was thus able to confirm the explanation for the illuminated wake.

One morning we noted that the convoy ahead had split into two, one half heading through the Madagascar Strait bound for the Middle East, and the other half continuing towards India. A groan could be heard above the clug of the engines when *Yoma* followed that part of the convoy bound for Bombay. With this parting of the ways came the sure knowledge that it would be several years before any of us could hope to see home again.

CHAPTER TWO

Hot and Dry

The summer of 1942 saw the medical communities of the garrison towns of India continuing a way of life they had enjoyed for decades. They were not disturbed by the news of Dunkirk or the Battle of Britain and they were even less concerned by the minor military skirmishes on the Maungdaw-Buthidaung road, a thousand miles away in Burma. The Indian Medical Service families lived in their well-appointed bungalows and were served by a host of servants including *ayahs* (nursemaids), *dhobis* (washerman), *bhistis* (water carriers), *punka-wallahs* (fan operators), sweepers (toilet attendants), a *syce* (groom), a *chowkidhar* (night watchman) and a cook. Bearers (personal servants) laid out clothing and were even available to dress and undress the Sahib and his Memsahib. Newcomers were required to make a formal call to leave specially printed visiting cards and in due course there would probably be an invitation to tea or for drinks. Mornings were spent on social calls or a visit to the club; afternoons were a time of rest and before sundown there might be another club visit for a bathe, tennis and dinner. On special mess nights the officers would don their full-dress uniforms and sit round a table decorated with flowers and regimental silver. After the dinner and the drinking of toasts, a unit band might provide music for dancing.

Into this world of tradition came the 80th British General Hospital. After disembarkation in Bombay, we were ushered past the Gateway to India into the railway station. Because of Gandhi riots we were not officially permitted to go sight-seeing but some managed to get a limited impression of the city, the pavements of which were decorated by the red sputum of the betel-nut chewers. For a few of us, the greater part of this first day was spent playing bridge in a railway carriage parked in a siding. Meals were taken from our billycans – bully beef at one end and tinned fruit at the other. That evening the troop train carrying the personnel and equipment of the 80th moved on its way towards the Deccan.

At the first halt, before the train began its slow ascent of the darkening slopes of the Western Ghats, advice was sought for a soldier who was in considerable pain from a whitlow. The only available treatment was two-hourly hot fomentations; for these the train was brought to a halt and the driver blew steam from the engine to fill a tin can with boiling water. The soaks were continued throughout the night and next morning, using a razor blade, it was possible to evacuate the pus from the offending finger.

Before noon, the train reached Secunderabad station where there was no welcoming carpet. No one expected us and no one wanted a 200-bedded hospital which some said was too small and others thought was too large. There was no readily available accommodation and, after several frustrating hours, it was decided that the 80th BGH might be housed in Plassy lines, which originally had been built for cavalry during World War 1. These hutments and stables were near Trimulgerry, some eight miles from the station; since no transport was available it was decided that we, carrying full kit, should march to the quarters. During the hot August afternoon, we mad Europeans, with our pale knees, laboured to complete this forced march before sundown. Many fell by the wayside with heat exhaustion and diarrhoea; those of us who completed the trip were rewarded with splitting headaches which took some time to respond to an intake of fluid and salt.

When at length we had recovered from the rigours of our march, we made such adjustments as we could to the stabling of the Plassy lines. Once the men were established, with cookhouse, quarters and latrines, a site had to be selected for the officers' mess and a conveniently large building of the bungalow-type, was chosen. I well remember our first evening meal in it. The hurricane lamps attracted all manner of insect life which covered the table, floor and food. One particular beetle, when crushed, emitted a most obnoxious odour which effectively removed any remaining appetite. It would be a gross understatement to say that, at this point, morale was very low.

Gradually the unit adjusted to the heat and the flies. Men no longer allowed their meals to be swiped by watchful kitehawks hovering over the cookhouse. To keep all occupied there were drills, parades, courts of enquiry, courts martial, Urdu lessons and all-night route marches. Gilroy Glass was good at organising these nocturnal wanderings, which usually started at 2200 hours. It was remarkable how often he turned up to review his troops prior to such an excursion and then, at the last moment, turn to me and say:

'Sandy, I have got a return of that pain in my big toe; you'd better take them on your own tonight.'

I did not mind the march so much nor his lame excuses but my strong objection was to being called 'Sandy'. As I had joined the 80th at the last moment before embarkation and since in the unit there was already a padre called 'Jack', Gilroy arbitrarily decided that I must be given a different Christian name.

It was frequently my lot to lead the column in a large circle, past paddy fields and through sleeping villages; there would be a ten-minute rest each hour and eventually, after dawn, we reached camp in time for breakfast. In the cool of the night the marches were really quite pleasant, but later in the morning the operating list would tend to drag and after lunch, I was more than ready to snatch a couple of hours of shut-eye.

On one occasion, the prospect of a visit by some brass hat stimulated Gilroy Glass to try to get the men of the 80th to drill like guardsmen. After many practice parades, the day arrived when the great man was to carry out the inspection. The men were to be drawn up in square formation. Two companies went through the motions of getting into the proper position, then the third section was marched up by our medical specialist, Bill Wallace, who halted his men and then shouted the command 'Right Turn!'. This resulted in the men turning their backs on the general but Bill quickly restored the situation by a smart 'Right About, Turn!'. No doubt the general was impressed but after this incident, Gilroy seemed to lose his drill obsession.

There was some brightening of the outlook when the first mail arrived from home and when it eventually dawned upon the higher authorities that trained medical personnel might be more usefully employed than in playing at soldiers. The 80th's complement of Queen Alexandra nursing sisters who had travelled out to India with the unit, on reaching Secunderabad were, under the wing of a matron, housed in special guarded quarters. Soon they were allocated to duties in the military hospitals where, quite apart from nursing and raising the morale of patients, they found themselves in great demand socially. With thousands of troops in training in the area, it was not surprising that a limited number of white women attracted a large following. Even the most ill-favoured ones who previously had never had a boy friend, now could command a wide choice of suitors. Our little group was soon split up. The medical specialist, Bill Wallace, was posted as physician to a 3,000 bedded hospital in Poona, but later returned to the British Military Hospital at Trimulgerry; the pathologist, Maurice Joseph, was sent off as a regimental medical officer; finally I took over the surgical division of the BMH.

Before a shared bungalow became available in the hospital precinct, I had to make bicycle trips from and back to Plassy lines. In the early hours of one morning, I was called for an emergency operation and set off on my hired bicycle. As I sped down-hill past the cemetery, with the head-lamp providing the only spark of illumination in a black night, suddenly there was the flapping of heavy wings and I was struck in the face and chest by what, at first I took to be some disembodied spirit; however, I quickly realised that I had collided with a large flying fox, or fruit bat, which no doubt also had received a shock. Having gathered my bicycle and self from the side of the road, I completed the journey to the hospital, where a tot of brandy steadied my shaking hands.

At the BMH there was routine peacetime type of surgery to be carried out. Operating lists usually started at 0700 hours and finished by noon. The officer commanding, a regular in the Indian Medical Service, ran the hospital as he had done for many years and he never varied the routine of his weekly round of inspection. With his entourage, the same route would be followed, the same questions would be asked and, in the kitchen, the same plate would be inspected; the orderlies well-versed in the procedure, made a point of having this particular plate especially cleaned for the visit. Colonel Grellier was essentially a kindly man who concerned him-

(*Top*) Urdu lessons at Trimulgerry.
(*Bottom*) Gilroy Glass and the author lead 80th BGH on the return from an all night route march

self about the well-being of patients, men and officers. His strong support for his staff was demonstrated at a Court of Enquiry which followed an unfortunate incident at the hospital. It happened that Bill Wallace, Captain Austin and I required a fourth for tennis at the club. Captain Roy Turner, who was listed as Orderly Officer for the day, agreed to make up the quartet after he found a Captain Griffiths to stand in for him. Griffiths, who a couple of days previously had shaved his head bald as a form of protest against authority, was still in a disgruntled frame of mind, and without informing anyone, had persuaded some junior officer to take over the duty.

On this particular evening, a medical general came into reception with his adjutant, who had been bitten by a dog; prophylactic measures against rabies had to be given. It was some considerable time before the stand-in for the stand-in orderly officer could be located and when he eventually turned up, he had no idea where the anti-rabies serum was kept. A nursing orderly was found to unlock the special cupboard but the substitute medical officer, new to India, had no clue about the administration of the injection. By this time the general, red with anger, seized the syringe and he himself gave the injections into the abdominal wall of his aide. The aide promptly fainted and there was the call for brandy which could not be immediately produced. The orderly officer went to look for some, but by the time he returned the General had stamped out of the hospital, dragging his unfortunate aide with him, so the orderly officer drank the brandy himself.

At the Court of Enquiry the next day, Colonel Grellier fully supported his junior staff and maintained that orderly officers had his full permission to find substitutes without any prior consultation. The findings of the court were that no one was really to blame for this unusual and unfortunate train of events. It was noticeable that within a few days, the Colonel was posted elsewhere and his imminent retirement was brought forward.

During the next few months, I was fortunate to have my own surgical work to do, especially when many others had little opportunity for employment in the spheres of their speciality. One evening there came a call from Professor Kahn in Osmania Hospital, Hyderabad. He asked for an opinion from both specialists of the

British Military Hospital. Lieutenant Colonel Preston was available as physician and I went along to provide the surgical opinion. The problem turned out to be a very ill boy who had developed bowel paralysis following an appendix operation. Intensive conservative measures had failed and Lieutenant Colonel Preston did not consider the problem to be one for a physician. After much discussion, it was agreed that an enterostomy (drainage of the bowel) should be carried out under local anaesthesia.

With the professor assisting and the gallery crowded with students, I carried out this small operation in the magnificent theatre luxuriously equipped by the Nizam of Hyderabad. Every type of expensive instrument was available, but I was not altogether happy about the effect of the powerful lights, which attracted all manner of flying insects to hover under the glare and settle on the bowel exposed in the operation wound. However, no one else seemed to be concerned about what, for them, must have been nothing unusual. Twenty-four hours after operation the bowel had regained its tone and the boy was on the way to full recovery.

A week later, accompanied by radiologist Captain Alan Lamballe, I paid another visit to the patient. As we entered the city, police whistles were blown and all traffic was brought to a halt at the roadside. Then along the street came a small, ancient, Austin car carrying the Nizam; once he had passed, traffic moved again and we continued our trip. We found the boy to be making sound progress and our visit coincided with a visit from his mother who was in 'purdah' and therefore hidden behind screens at the patient's bedside.

An older brother, who spoke fluent English, invited us to join the family for tea. This turned out to be a somewhat unusual event as our hostess served us without, at any time, revealing more than a bare forearm and a bejewelled hand. After tea, we were given a couple of green betel leaf cones and instructed on how they were used. On leaving the hospital, we, for the first and last time, tried out betel chewing. Initially there was a pleasant aromatic taste associated with a mild local anaesthetic effect, later followed by the stimulation of profuse salivation. As we laboured uphill on our bicycles we were soon decorating the wayside with volumes of red spit. It was many hours before the salivary stimulation subsided

The author, November 1942

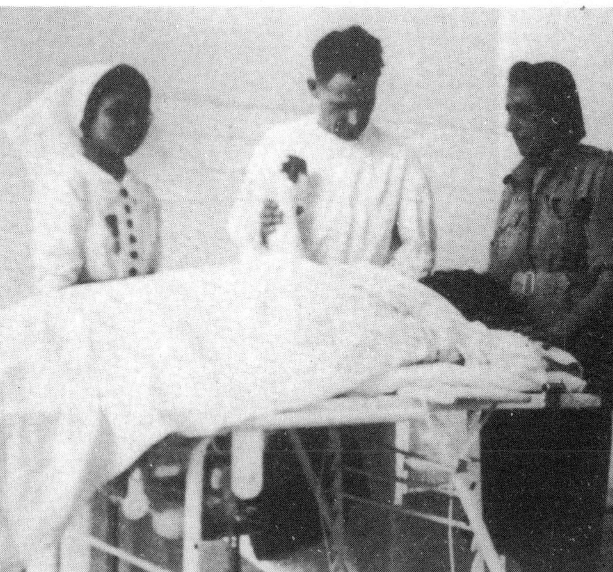

(*Top left*) The author and W. D. Wallace at Trimulgerry.
(*Top right*) The Sikh with a Colles fracture at the Indian Hospital, Trimulgerry.
(*Bottom*) The British Military Hospital at Trimulgerry

and it was several days before we could rid our teeth of the red stain.

Stationed in the area, the 14th BGH was at this time a non-functioning hospital. The O/C of their surgical division, John Bruce, had been detached to travel round India to sort out problems and try to improve the standard of surgery in military hospitals, many of which were part of the old Indian Medical Service. He told me that in one hospital where there was a very poor performance, he found that the chief surgeon had no surgical qualifications. On enquiry, it was discovered that this man, who had a lucrative private practice as a side-line, had filled in his record forms in such a way as to suggest that he had the FRCS. Actually he was a Fellow of the Royal Geographical Society and had written the 'G' to look like a 'C'.

When John periodically returned to Secunderabad, it was his custom to look me up and since he was doing no practical work, ask if I could find any operation for him to keep his eye in. Sometimes there was nothing more than a list of hernias but once he was highly delighted to have the opportunity to remove a large growth of the kidney. It was a strange situation for the future Professor of Surgery of Edinburgh to rely on me to let him carry out the odd operation.

A few miles from the BMH was a large Indian Military Hospital to which I was called from time to time to consult with the Indian surgeon. On one occasion he phoned to tell me that he had just admitted a British soldier who had sustained a severe head injury in a road accident. When I suggested that he transfer the patient to the BMH, he said that he could not take the responsibility of authorising the move in case the man died and he insisted that I came over at once. Transport was sent for me. The Indian driver of the truck demonstrated his skill at the wheel by keeping his foot hard down on the accelerator and his thumb on the horn as we weaved at speed past pedestrians, cyclists and bullock carts without damaging anything apart from my nerves. At the hospital I reviewed the patient, who had a large hole on the left side of his skull with lacerated brains protruding, and gave the necessary authority for the transfer. As the bearers moved to lift the stretcher into the ambulance the surgeon exclaimed:

'Stop! This patient is a road accident case and he has not been given the regulation injection ATS.'

I could not refrain from replying that if the poor fellow lived long enough to develop tetanus, he would be a very lucky man. Back in the theatre at the BMH we found that the situation was quite hopeless and in spite of our efforts the man died in a couple of hours. A week later, another head injury was dead on arrival at the BMH. At Bolarum, a pilot in training had flown his aircraft at full throttle into the control tower at the airfield. His head had taken the full force of the impact and yet the skin had remained intact. The mixture of shattered skull, blood clot and brains filled the featureless sac which once had been a head. Only once before can I recollect having seen a more ghastly remains; in the steel works in Rotherham, a man got his arm caught in a cold rolling mill which drew him completely through a space of one foot by six inches and deposited his body on the other side, ironed out flat.

In due course, the Indian surgeon was replaced by Major Frost who, by a fortunate coincidence, had been my house surgeon at Rotherham Hospital before he had joined the Indian Medical Service. He was married to a Rotherham nurse and with their three-year-old son, they were settled in the garrison married quarters where frequently I was well entertained by them. Before Frost's arrival there had been a gap of a few weeks when I had to stand in for surgical cases at the Indian Hospital; this was my first experience in dealing with Indian patients and staff, whose ideas then seemed quite strange. One problem was created by a Sikh with a Colles fracture; he insisted that for religious reasons the steel bracelet round his damaged wrist should not be removed. After manipulation and correction of the deformity, there was no alternative but to incorporate the ring within the plaster, the removal of which at a later date turned out to be quite a harassing exercise. One morning, the nursing orderlies had found that the autoclave used for steam sterilisation was not reaching the proper pressure; to cure this they effectively fastened down the safety valve. Within an hour, the resulting spectacular explosion effectively wrecked the sterilising room which, at the time, was fortunately clear of any personnel.

At irregular intervals during the months spent at the BMH, we had visits from Nabi Bux, a stout, elderly Kashmeri who would appear at our quarters on his bicycle loaded with a large white bundle. He waited patiently until it was convenient for an audience. Then, sitting cross-legged on the veranda, like the showman he was, he gradually revealed his fabulous wares. These included intricately carved sandal-wood boxes, elaborately decorated evening jackets, prayer mats, silver filigree ornaments and Kashmere woollen shawls so delicate that they could be threaded through a wedding ring. After a little bartering, satisfactory deals were eventually concluded. With some purchases, chance was taken to send them back to the UK; others were stored in the tin trunk, liberally sprinkled with *neen* leaves and camphor balls to deter the ants.

From a high-class jeweller's shop in Secunderabad, I bought for my wife a platinum eternity ring. Naturally my concern was to prevent it being stolen and I seriously considered making a small incision on my abdominal wall under local anaesthesia, then inserting the ring into the subcutaneous fat and finally stitching the skin. This idea was abandoned when, on consideration, it seemed likely that the sterilisation of the ring carried with it the risk that the setting of the diamonds might be disturbed. As an alternative, the ring was hidden in my tin trunk amongst the goods purchased from Nabi Bux. That trunk went through many hair-raising experiences but, eventually it reached home with its contents intact.

In civilian life, it is usual to regard symptoms as being genuine even although on examination there may be no abnormal findings. The opposite approach was required in the army. A mile from the hospital, the area 'glass house' provided a small but steady flow of problem prisoners who, having got tired of doing everything at the double, decided to try malingering for a change. Some elected to produce specimens of urine to which they had added blood. The symptom of haematuria always requires further investigation and in such cases, in order to exclude bladder or kidneys as possible sources, examination by the cystoscope is required. Where there was a strong suspicion that the man was swinging the lead, the instrument was passed along the urethra without any anaesthetic. The news of this somewhat uncomfortable examination filtered back to the prison inmates, who produced no further blood-stained specimens of urine.

In those soldiers complaining of acute abdominal pain without any supporting signs, it was at first difficult to exclude such conditions as acute appendicitis. The orthodox method of dealing with an undiagnosed abdominal pain was to put the patient on clear fluids only and give no sedatives which might obscure signs; check of the pulse rate and temperature together with re-examination of the abdomen at regular intervals was needed during this period of observation. After twenty-four hours, increase in the pulse rate, the appearance of muscle guarding and other signs would indicate that operation was required. In the malingerer there would be no such changes; after forty-eight hours he no longer complained of pain and he would be asking for food. Another twenty-four hours would see 'the patient' utterly ravenous. After a further day or so on fluids only, he was admitting his offence and begging to be returned to the 'glass house', where no doubt he spread the news that faked abdominal pain was not to be recommended.

During the stay at Secunderabad, opportunity was taken to view the nearby famous Golconda ruins which in the past had been a treasure house of the East. On another occasion, there was a conducted tour of the modern Osmania University which was the Nizam's pride. A week later a memorable visit was paid to a huge leper colony near Nyzamabad. This isolated community had, for many years, been run by a medical missionary, Dr Dewer; he and his wife had trained the no longer infectious lepers in the nursing care and treatment of the more seriously afflicted. On the rounds of the hospital, examples of all types of leprosy were demonstrated including those distressing terminal cases in whom features and limbs had been grossly eroded. Before the journey back, we were entertained to a special meal which included fresh fish picked out of a stock pool in the grounds. Locally, a self-important Indian contractor to the BMH, offered to arrange for a few of us to inspect a very special Hindu temple renowned for its phallic symbols. He met us at the entrance and we were told to wait whilst he sought permission from the priests. From the side of the forecourt there soon arose the sounds of a fierce argument, with shouting and screaming going on for several minutes. Then our would-be guide sheepishly re-appeared to state mildly: 'They say no!'.

Quite apart from these activities, the time spent in the Deccan

(*Top left*) A hot bath from the cold tap.
(*Top right*) Child leper taking a specimen from a chronic patient.
(*Bottom*) School for leper children at Nyzamabad

was not wasted, as it afforded an opportunity for acclimatisation. Thanks to tennis, swimming and early morning PT, general health was improved in readiness for the difficult times ahead. Even so, it was later found that in Burma a temperature of 90 degrees with a humidity of 90, was less easily tolerated than a dry heat of 120 degrees in the hottest part of India. It was of interest to find that in the early evening it was possible to enjoy a really hot soak in a canvas bath filled from the single 'cold water' tap; the pipes supplying the quarters were just under the surface of the soil which failed to insulate them from the penetrating heat of the afternoon sun.

Protective spinal pads were no longer employed against sunstroke, but we arrived in the sub-continent wearing the same type of *topi* which had seen service in the tropics in World War 1. Initially, drill jackets were worn over shirt with collar and tie. This uniform however was soon replaced by the open-necked bush shirt which was not tucked into the shorts, thus allowing more air to circulate. It was not long before the old-fashioned pith helmet gave way to the light-weight cork *topi*. After we reached Burma, the *topi* disappeared and the usual headgear was the Australian type of bush hat which gave excellent protection from sun and rain. Only on rare occasions was it considered desirable to change the bush hat for a tin helmet. Light-weight green battle dress was substituted for the bush shirt and at sundown, shorts were changed for long trousers tucked into the boots. The possibility of sunstroke and heat exhaustion had to be considered as a hazard but, in due course, after graduated exposure, it was demonstrated that during the day, one could wear no more than hat, shorts, socks and boots without harm, provided there was an adequate intake of salt and fluid. When the body is lacking salt, a drink of tea laced with several spoonfuls of salt instead of sugar, does not even have a salty taste.

In Burma, I was fortunate in having the services of an outstanding anaesthetist, Major George Quayle. At the BMH Secunderabad, there had been a time when operation lists became a nightmare because of an unsatisfactory anaesthetist. This elderly ill-tempered captain was supposed to be a specialist, but regularly failed to get the patients properly under and when I suggested a change to spinal anaesthetics, it was rare for him to find the correct position for the lumbar puncture needle. Matters came to a head when Gilroy asked me to support his recommendation that this man should be promoted to the rank of major. I reminded him that I had already let him have my report about the unsatisfactory anaesthetics and I would not support such a promotion, nor would I tolerate the situation any longer. Unfortunately, Gilroy had already submitted the documents to Colonel Vince who, finding I had refused to sign, called a meeting to discuss the problem. I made it quite clear what my feelings were and refused to give my signature. I never heard the final outcome of this disagreement as shortly afterwards my posting came through.

Gradually it became evident that increasing numbers of combatant units were training in the area. Captain Rogers, after attending the hospital for some minor surgical condition, suggested a visit to his unit at Borarum, a few miles north of Trimulgerry where he was in charge of tank testing. This was a most interesting afternoon and I availed myself of the opportunity to drive a General Lee heavy tank round the test course. That evening, before supper, Captain Roger's pet mongoose Tikki, introduced itself. It was a fascinating little animal and there was no limit to its inquisitiveness. Any visitor had to be prepared to have his pockets searched most thoroughly and when the mongoose tired of this entertainment, it would disappear into the garden for a short time and then bring back a snake with which it would play on the mat before making the final kill.

Another invitation was given by an ex-patient who had come from the United States to introduce into India the first squadron of Vengeance dive bombers. He was most enthusiastic on the merits of the plane, which he claimed could take off on its own, provided the controls were properly set. All the features of this marvellous aircraft were demonstrated and included was a special tutorial on the method of lining up the bomb sight during the dive on the target. Some twelve months later, I was again destined to see Lee tanks and Vengeance dive bombers, but this time they were in action against the Japanese.

On an inspection visit from Brigadier Cameron, who had taught me medicine in Edinburgh, I pointed out that it seemed rather a

Testing a General Lee tank

waste that I should have been brought thousands of miles merely to be engaged in civilian surgery. He hinted that soon a wind of change would be blowing through the medical centres of Secunderabad. Within a few weeks, a new military hospital was opened up a mile down the road from the old BMH and Lieutenant Colonel Norrish came as officer in charge of the surgical division. Soon all patients were transferred to the new hospital and the handing over was completed. For me there came the posting order to proceed to Maungdaw, Arakan, to take over the command of No 7 Indian Mobile Surgical Unit.

CHAPTER THREE

Advance and Retreat

From Secunderabad in the Deccan of India, there lay ahead a journey of almost a thousand miles to be covered by train, river-steamer, train again and finally truck into Burma. I was soon to learn how heavily Burma, with its climate, its diseases, its jungle, its long line of communications and its invaders loaded the dice against the sick and wounded, while we whose medical efforts were directed toward overcoming these adverse conditions were halfway to defeat before the game began.

On 3rd May 1943, I settled my debts, drew out advance pay of 400 rupees, collected travel warrants, did my packing and sent a cable to my wife to let her know that my future address would be with No 7 Indian Mobile Surgical Unit, India Command. That evening the officers of 80 BGH entertained me to a farewell dinner at Montgomery's restaurant, at which I was presented with a carved wooden cigarette box bearing the insignia of the hospital. Before noon next day, my friends were at Secunderabad station to see me off. As the train left a couple of hours late, our farewells were, to say the least, protracted.

It was dark when I reached Beswarda junction, twelve hours before my connection with the Madras-Calcutta mail was due. I spent some time in the refreshment room, then went to the waiting room, where I attempted to get some sleep in a hard, unyielding wooden chair. But my efforts were in vain. Not only was the chair a monument to the discomfort of all travellers, if I did succeed in nodding off for a moment I was abruptly awakened by a family of rats which scampered intermittently around the room, squeaking as they pattered over the floorboards.

But even the longest night must end. At first light the mail train

Leaving Secunderabad for Arakan

steamed magnificently into the little station, and once aboard, my journey became more comfortable. I shared a compartment with an American officer, Major Fort, who proved a most entertaining companion. With the uninhibited friendliness of most Americans, he at once began a conversation. By the time we had eaten breakfast at a wayside halt and provided ourselves with tinned beer, mangoes, pineapples and a luncheon parcel, I knew all about his home town, his boyhood and his 'folks' – a charming young wife and two blond children, whose snapshots he extracted from his wallet and shyly tendered for my appraisal. And throughout the long day the monotonous landscape of India flashed by. The only memorable sight came as the train ponderously laboured over the long, girdered bridge across the River Godavari; the vista of distant mountains gleaming through the thin blue haze, filled my mind with a nostalgic memory of the far-away English Lake District.

When we approached the suburbs of Calcutta, the train slowed down to a crawl, never exceeding 10 mph, negotiating points, junctions and level crossings until it finally crossed the high bridge over the Hoogley river and came to a halt in Howrah station, some three hours late. It was not difficult to find a porter; no sooner had I stepped on the platform than a tall Sikh swung my heavy tin trunk on to his turbaned head and immediately set out towards the station entrance. Carrying the remainder of my luggage, I followed as quickly as I could; although the porter himself was soon lost in the milling crowd, it was possible to keep track of his progress by following my tin trunk as it swayed above the sea of bobbing heads. A short taxi ride brought me to the Grand Hotel, which had been taken over to accommodate officers in transit; there were no vacant beds, so after an evening meal, I had no option but to spend the night on an easy chair in the spacious ornate lounge. At least it was an improvement on the one at Beswarda junction.

Colourful Chowringhee extended for a mile beyond the Grand Hotel. A wide road crowded with taxis, trams, tongas and bicycle-drawn rickshaws separated the seething masses on the pavement from the open space of the arid brown *maidan*. It was said that during a walk along this street, just as in Princes Street, Edinburgh, one was sure to bump into some acquaintance. And amongst the representatives of all sections of the Allied Services mingling with the *dhoti*-clad natives of the city, it was not long before I encountered Major Lockie who, years previously in Edinburgh, had given me tutorials in midwifery. He was now resident medical officer at the Red Fort barracks; I was unable to accept his invitation to dine there that evening but on my next visit to Calcutta, for a surgical conference, it was possible to enjoy his hospitality.

After this meeting I continued my stroll past well-stocked shops, places of entertainment, restaurants and highly exclusive clubs. On the other side of the pavement were the gutter pedlars pushing their wares. It would have been possible to barter for highly-coloured sweetmeats, large well padded boxes of dates or for bottles of Scotch from which the whisky had been aspirated through a syringe and replaced by tea or urine. Puppies, monkeys and parrots were on offer, as well as sparrows painted yellow to simulate canaries. Absent from Chowringhee were the untouchable sweepers who, before the war, eked out their meagre incomes in the poorer quarters of the city. Prior to the replacement of solid quinine by mepacrine in the treatment of malaria, the sweepers when emptying the 'thunder boxes' (commodes) searched for tablets in the motions. Quinine sulphate was not readily soluble and it was not uncommon for tablets to pass through the alimentary tract little changed. The sweeper would pick out these slightly smaller tablets, wash them and put them in a bottle for sale to their even less fortunate compatriots.

To seek some relief from the humid afternoon, I went to the Lighthouse Cinema which was air-conditioned. The sudden change from moist heat to dry cold gave me my first experience of the skin irritation known as prickly heat, and after an hour I was glad to be back on the pavements of Chowringhee.

That evening, after threading my way over and around bodies of homeless Indians already settling on the platform for the night, I left Sealdah station a couple of hours before midnight. By first light, the train came to a halt at Sirajganj on the western bank of the Brahmaputra. The oblique crossing of this vast muddy river, whose distant bank was too far away for any detail to be made out, was made on a heavily laden paddle steamer which slowly churned its way upstream whilst I breakfasted on tea and a miniature hard boiled egg. At Raganmathganj, transfer was made to a somewhat primitive train which stopped at every small station and eventually reached Chittagong in the early hours of the next morning. During the journey across Bengal, I had felt somewhat out of place as I was the only European travelling towards the east; there was not the slightest sign of any military activity, not even the sight of a single sepoy. At Chittagong however, after spending the remainder of the night in the station's upstairs waiting room, I was pleasantly surprised to find a few BOR's (British Other Ranks) who directed me to the rail travel office. At noon each day a single train, running on a narrow-gauge line, left for Dohazari; the creaking rattling journey ended a couple of hours later in the small dusty township with its single storey buildings and dumps of stores.

Dohazari was the end of the line and at that time represented the gateway to Burma. My kit, consisting of tin trunk, suitcase and bedroll around a camp bed, was transferred from the side of the rail tracks to the shelter of a long hut which served as the station, and I began a search for someone who might be able to assist my onward journey. No breeze ruffled the tall palm trees and the oppressive heat had brought all activity to a standstill. A few days before, a minor Japanese air raid had taken place doing little damage. So, although it had stimulated the digging of some slit trenches, the township had quickly relapsed into a general state of apathy and uncertainty. Many personnel were enjoying an afternoon's rest, popularly called 'Charpoy bashing'. Eventually, after many fruitless efforts, a co-operative officer was located and, through him, contact was made with an RAF unit which was evacuating equipment from the south. It was then possible to get on transport to travel along the way as far as Ramu where a non-functioning Field Ambulance had pitched its tents in the jungle, a hundred yards from the road.

The officer commanding the Field Ambulance provided the information that both combatant and medical units were in the process of joining the retreat out of Burma. He had no idea where any ADMS (Assistant Director Medical Services) might be located to give direction, but he assured me that the Japanese had re-occupied Maungdaw and a search for No 7 Indian Mobile Surgical Unit in that town was not likely to prove very rewarding. Over an evening meal with the officers of the Field Ambulance, it was evident that morale was low; their main interest was in how quickly they might get back into India. Accommodation for the night was provided for me in a 40 lb tent, open back and front. There was just space on one side for the camp bed with its mosquito netting. From the surrounding jungle, the jackal calls combined with the heat to make sleep difficult. During the early hours, a particularly loud outburst of nearby cries culminated in what sounded like a fight; then suddenly one of the beasts, loudly howling and hotly pursued by another, rushed through the entrance, past my bed and out through the back of my tent. After this episode, the tent flaps were closed and only fitful sleep was possible.

The dawn came cool, bright and peaceful. Although a lie-in would have been welcome, it was necessary to find south-bound transport, for I seemed to be the only individual advancing whilst everyone else was retreating. Eventually I was installed in a RA truck destined to collect personnel from artillery units near Bawli Bazar. The trip began after an early breakfast. The rough, solitary road into Arakan wandered through the villages of Ramkapapha-long and Ukhia towards Tumbru. In many places along the route the jungle was dense and the erstwhile green foliage was, on each side, covered with the red dust raised by the north-bound trans-ports. A few miles short of Tumbru, a fork left led into areas in which the trees had thinned to be replaced by a profusion of bamboo and elephant grass. The truck, which had been finding even the moderate gradients a severe trial, eventually coughed to a halt under the shade of a large tree overhanging the road. The driver, after unsuccessful attempts to restart the vehicle, thought that further effort should be delayed until after lunch, by which time he hoped that the engine would have cooled.

The early afternoon sun did not help the cooling process and the engine still failed to show the slightest spark of life. Whilst the driver and his mate sweated under the bonnet of the truck, small convoys and some light guns passed on their way out of Burma; no one seemed interested in the broken down truck facing in the opposite direction. At times, the strange eerie silence of the jungle would be broken by a chorus of activity from the crickets and at irregular intervals there could be heard a most peculiar call which the driver said came from the 'Tuk-Tu bird', but later I learned that this spasmodic loud noise in the heat of the afternoons was produced by a large lizard. The troops assumed that the noise came from a bird and used a less polite name for the producer of this recurring irritating call.

As the afternoon wore on, the traffic moving back from forward areas became a trickle and eventually it ceased altogether. The thought crossed our minds that, at any time, a Jap patrol would next appear, but relief came in the shape of an RAF truck bound for Bawli Bazar. The RA vehicle was abandoned and we continued the journey into more open country; dry paddy fields were backed by the first sight of the jungle-clad Mayo Ridge. The road meandered between hillocks swathed in olive green, flapping banana trees, interspersed with bamboo thickets and capped with betel nut palms.

Eventually the Pruma *chaung* (tidal river) came into view on the right; the Pruma which was at least a hundred yards wide was the main tributary of the River Naf. The only road across it was carried, at this time, by a frail bamboo bridge which creaked and groaned under the weight of the light truck. Once over the bridge, we could see the bamboo *bashas* of Bawli Bazar, lying between the paddy fields and the Mayo Ridge. Near Bawli, a truck wearing a red cross was flagged down and from the driver, Quartermaster Taylor, I obtained the information that No 7 Mobile Surgical Unit had attached itself to No 46 Field Ambulance, of which he was the quartermaster. In his company, the few miles down the Bawli-Maungdaw road were completed before sundown and the first welcome meeting with No 7 took place.

The Australian Major Reg Hooper was to be given a break from his duties and I was to succeed him as officer in command of the unit. From Wales, Major George Quayle, anaesthetist and former St George's Hospital rugger forward, was to remain, to give valuable support over the many months that lay ahead. Hooper and Quayle gave me the story of the unit's earlier activities after it had first been mobilised at Jhansi, India in 1942, under the command of Major J. Saxton, IMS.

Major Hooper, who took over the unit in February 1943, brought No 7 into the Arakan to attach itself to No 15 Casualty Clearing

Station in Maungdaw. This dusty, sprawling, bamboo town, sited where the Tat *chaung* joined the River Naf, was of considerable military importance as the supply port and western terminal of the Maungdaw-Buthidaung road, a disused railway track which traversed the Mayo Ridge through The Tunnels. Travelling in a flat-bottomed hospital ship, the Missouri, George Quayle had reached Maungdaw to find No 7 sorting out equipment and learning how to pitch tents. South of Maungdaw, the 14th Indian Division, in attempting to reach Akyab via Foul Point, had received a decisive check at Donbaik. Successive attacks over open ground had failed to overcome the Japanese, who were established in honeycombed defensive systems. A regiment of the Inniskillins was wiped out and casualties soon came flooding back to Maungdaw. With four tables in the operating tent, the CCS was working day and night and No 7, in their own theatre, were dealing with the more major cases. Since the seriously wounded were taking too long to reach Maungdaw, the unit was ordered south along the coast to Nahkaungdo (No-can-do) and pitched tents under a massive mango tree laden with ripe fruit. Work was carried out in four-hourly stretches with an hour's break between lists.

No 7 was the first mobile surgical unit to work in the Arakan and initially there had been some confusion as to where and how this new toy should be employed. When the unit was south of Maungdaw, it was suggested to Major Hooper that he should, with anaesthetist, a few men and a pannier of dressings and instruments, accompany landing attacks down the coast to carry out the necessary operations on the spot. This policy was not pursued after he had pointed out that no advantage was to be gained by attempting major surgery in the midst of a conflict. In addition, since surgeons had taken many years to learn their craft, it was not justifiable to risk losing them in activities in which their special skills could not be properly utilised. The casualties from such attacks would be better served by ordinary first-aid measures provided by non-specialists; then there should be early transference of the wounded to a mobile surgical unit located at a Main Dressing Station, where major surgery could be carried out in relative safety and the patient could be properly cared for after his operation.

After some weeks of activity at Nahkaungdo, it became evident that attack had been turned into retreat. Having no transport of its own, the unit, at the last moment, was able to get hold of one of the trucks remaining in an artillery unit. The vehicle was grossly overloaded, with some personnel crammed in front and ten sepoys wedged horizontally under the canvas roof. The journey had barely started when the truck went off the road and overturned, miraculously without any serious injury being sustained! Thanks to winches from a gun-carriage, the situation was brought under control and the unit, in the very last truck, limped north to Maungdaw to link up once again with No 15 CCS.

Lieutenant-Colonel Cropper and the staff of the CCS were utterly exhausted after handling about a thousand casualties who were being evacuated by twice weekly visits of SS *Missouri* which was frequently attacked from the air. Once again, No 7 quickly set up their own theatre to concentrate on head, chest and abdominal wounds. In the midst of the chaos, George Quayle recalled that a 15 cwt truck drew up in a cloud of dust from which emerged a big fellow saying that he had brought some equipment for the unit. He was briefly thanked and waved on his way, after being told where to dump the crate which, when unpacked, was found to contain the first Boyle's anaesthetic machine to reach the Arakan. Only later was it discovered, with some embarrassment, that the visitor had been no other than the new ADMS, Brigadier Ambrose Meneces.

After a few weeks at full pressure, those remaining in Maungdaw realised that a Japanese attack would not be delayed for much longer. At 1800 hours, on what was to be a memorable night, all officers were ordered to report to the mess of the CCS. Sealed envelopes were handed out with the instruction that they were only to be opened in the event of a Japanese attack. The gist of the message was: 'First get rid of all patients by evacuation and then every man for himself.'

Just after sundown, a shot rang out to be followed by a burst of machine-gun fire. Then all hell broke loose and every gun in the neighbourhood opened up to pour tracer bullets in all directions. As the missiles whistled through the CCS everyone dived for cover and there was near panic. Quayle, after having escaped being shot at the entrance to a slit trench, first crawled and then sprinted to reach his own unit, where he found Hooper reading in bed and all the others soundly sleeping. No Japanese were involved in this full scale battle; it had been started by jittery, trigger-happy troops. Nevertheless, the gunfire continued throughout the night, exhausting the ammunition stock of the whole area. In spite of the torrents of bullets from all sides, not one caused an injury and the only casualty was an Indian sepoy, drowned in his attempt to escape across the River Naf. The events of that night were thereafter referred as 'The Maungdaw Tamasha' (show or party).

The following morning it came as a complete surprise to discover that the CCS had vanished, leaving equipment behind. Whilst awaiting orders, No 7 spent a useful few hours stocking up with theatre lights, drugs and a heavy rubber mat on which to stand the operating table. From the abandoned stores there were collected two Winchester bottles of absolute alcohol and a small bottle of Oleum Juniperi, in the hope that gin might be produced from these ingredients. This hope was dashed when it was discovered that Oleum Juniperi was, in fact, turpentine.

Whilst the motley crowd of No 7 was carrying away the spoils, a station wagon suddenly appeared and the unit formally met Brigadier Meneces. The looters, who were relieved at not being shot, instead received congratulations on their salvage efforts! The ADMS ordered a speedy evacuation to the area of Brigade Headquarters, the map reference being somewhere just south of Bawli Bazar. Before dusk, in some abandoned RAF trucks, the unit left Maungdaw to the Japs and journeyed north at the greatest possible speed.

By 0200 hours, on a pitchblack night, it was thought that the map reference had been reached but no Brigade HQ could be located. Reg Hooper and George Quayle set off in opposite directions and immediately became hopelessly lost. One of the trucks managed to get on to a dry paddy field and, without lights, wandered round and round trying to find an exit. Finally the search was given up and the two halves of the unit slept in the trucks to await the dawn. At daylight the unit re-grouped and found the proper bearing. The order was received to open up in a deserted native village occupied by No 46 Field Ambulance. The village,

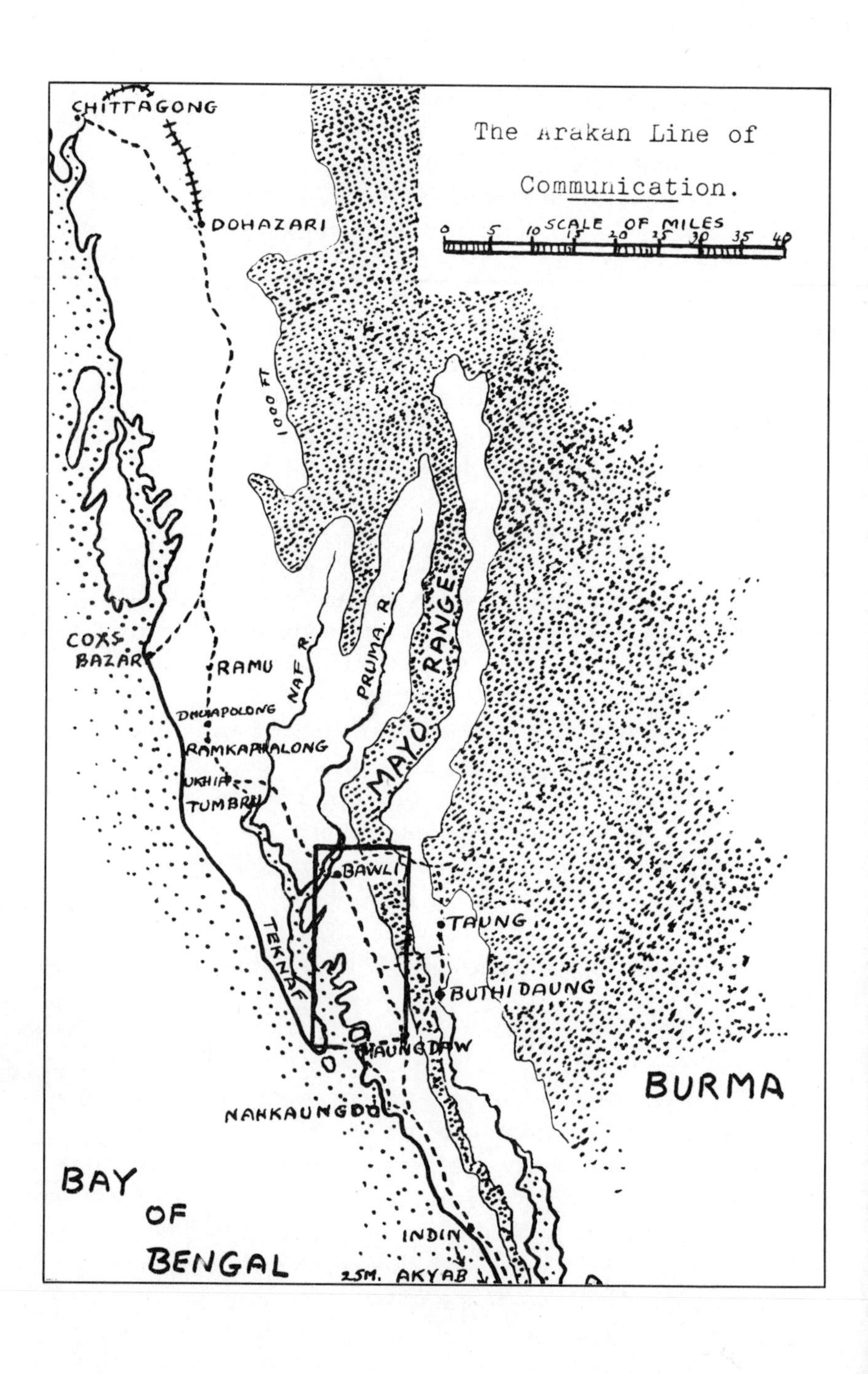

The Arakan Line of Communication.
SCALE OF MILES
0 5 10 15 20 25 30 35 40
CHITTAGONG
DOHAZARI
1000 FT
COXS BAZAR
RAMU
NAF R.
PRUMA R.
MAYO RANGE
RAMKAPHALONG
BAWLI
TAUNG
TEKNAF
BUTHIDAUNG
MAUNGDAW
NAHKAUNGDO
BURMA
BAY OF BENGAL
INDIN
25M. AKYAB

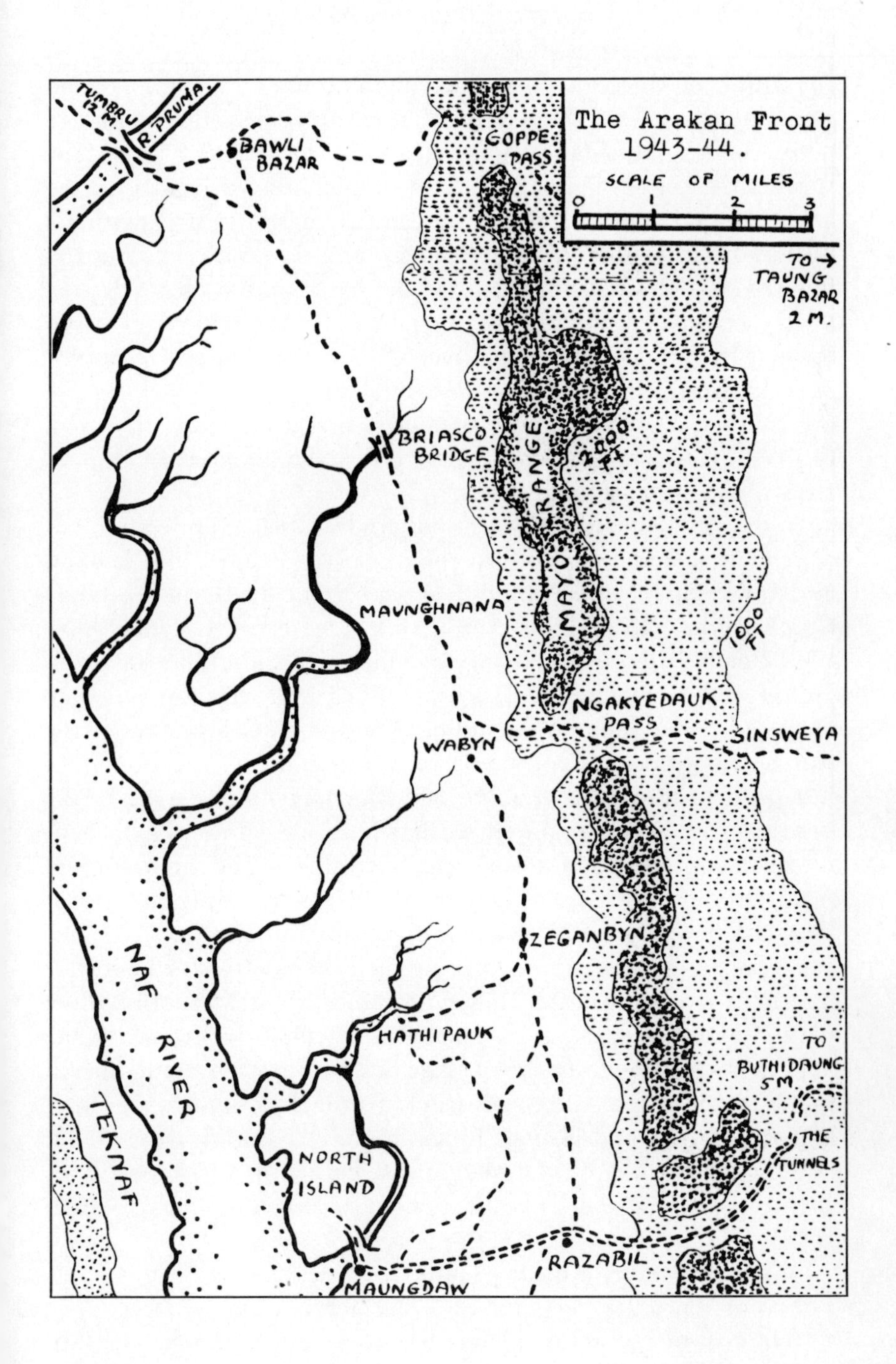
The Arakan Front
1943-44.
SCALE OF MILES
0
1
2
3
TUMBRU
12 M.
R. PRUMA
BAWLI
BAZAR
GOPPE
PASS
TO →
TAUNG
BAZAR
2 M.
BRIASCO
BRIDGE
MAYO RANGE
2000 FT
MAUNGHNANA
1000 FT
NGAKYEDAUK
PASS
SINSWEYA
WABYN
ZEGANBYN
NAF
RIVER
HATHIPAUK
TO
BUTHIDAUNG
5 M.
THE
TUNNELS
TEKNAF
NORTH
ISLAND
RAZABIL
MAUNGDAW

consisting of thirty to forty huts built from mud, bamboo and elephant grass, was grouped round a central pool shaded by mango trees. A long large *basha* was selected as theatre and in it some snags soon became apparent. Snakes had to be driven from the grass roof and this exercise produced volumes of dust. Additional dust came from the adjacent road, as any traffic raised clouds of fine red particles which penetrated the *basha* and formed a deposit over sterilised basins and instruments. This deposition was diminished by fixing thin netting over all openings but it was agreed that, in future, the operating theatre should be sited well clear of the main road. Many months later, when dust again created a problem, it was controlled by having the offending section of road strewn with wet banana leaves.

In the next few days, the unit had to deal with a limited number of casualties and it was whilst they were so engaged that I found and joined No 7 Indian Mobile Surgical Unit. The Burmese Officer Commanding No 46 Field Ambulance, Lieutenant-Colonel Shirezan, had been a contemporary of mine at Edinburgh University and, over the evening meal, we had much to discuss. At this time few would have thought, including Shirezan himself, that after the war he would occupy an important position in the government of independent Burma. After the late social evening, a visit to the quarter-master was required so that he could issue us with non-medical equipment in the shape of revolvers and ammunition. Apart from a little aerial activity the night was peaceful and at long last it was possible to catch up on my lost sleep.

Opportunity was afforded during the next twenty-four hours, for me to see No 7 at work dealing with minor wounds. Another quiet night was followed by a hot, peaceful morning during which the only activity came from the passage of small convoys along the red road. At intervals, after the trucks, straggling groups of tired-looking Indian and British infantry ambled northwards. About noon, a jeep swung off the road and screeched to a halt beside the theatre *basha*. A somewhat hot combatant brigadier emerged from the dust cloud to greet us with –

'What the hell is a medical unit doing here?'

To our reply that we were awaiting orders to move came:

'You will be getting no bloody orders, except from me. The Japs are no more than a few miles down the road so you'd better get your outfit across Bawli Bridge before it has to be blown!'

This information stimulated a hasty packing of equipment and speedy loading on to borrowed trucks. After a slight delay whilst the Indian members of the unit rounded up their chickens, No 7 followed the retreat and was across the bridge over the Pruma by 1400 hours. But the bridge was never blown, despite the brigadier's anxiety.

A few miles beyond the bridge, a halt was made and the unit moved off the road on to open ground near the north bank of the Pruma. Enquiries had eventually provided the instruction that No 7 was, at its own pace, to move back to join the Field Ambulance at Tumbru, some fourteen miles away. By this time it was late afternoon and very hot, so it was decided that the journey would be resumed the next day. As a special treat, the whole unit obtained considerable relief from a bathe in the salty, muddy waters of the nearby Pruma *chaung*. Having come to the conclusion that, for one night, it was hardly worth while unpacking and putting up tents, camp beds were lain out in the open.

As we settled for the night, there was not a cloud to hide the splendour of the heavens; at this time of the year in this latitude, both the North Star and the Southern Cross were clearly visible. After midnight, however, came our first taste of the so-called mango shower. Clouds had built up from the west and before dawn the mango shower had developed into a violent downpour which lasted for a couple of hours. Some of the unit sought shelter under the trucks, others stuck it out under bedding covered by ground sheets. The ground sheet certainly gave protection from direct penetration by the rain, but it failed to stop a gradual seepage of wetness through the corners and edges, so that eventually the only dry object in one's bed was the revolver under the pillow.

By daylight all clouds had disappeared, and a cold, soaking unit surfaced to start the drying out process. In the warming sun, bedding was spread out over the bushes on all sides, giving the appearance of an Indian laundry. Before the drying was complete, the unit had a visit from an irate colonel who, in no uncertain terms, pointed out that our display of dirty washing was an open invitation for any Japanese aircraft. Fortunately there was no visi-

'. . . bedding was spread out on all sides, giving the appearance of an Indian Laundry.'

tation from the Japs and after this fully justified rocket, the partially dried sheets were quickly bundled up. Trucks were shunted under cover of nearby trees until after the mid-day meal and then the unit moved on, to reach Tumbru in the late afternoon.

The operating theatre at Tumbra

CHAPTER FOUR

Hot and Wet

The village of Tumbru had been deserted by its inhabitants and the vacated bamboo *bashas* had been taken over by the No 46 Field Ambulance; additional huts were in the process of construction. Scrub-covered hillocks topped by the odd palm tree surrounded a flat dusty compound into which not even a whisper of breeze penetrated to soften the shimmering heat of this suntrap.

No 7 settled into their own tents between the hillocks, and a larger *basha* was adapted as an operating theatre which was soon in action to deal with mortar-shell and bullet wound casualties. Several tents hidden in the surrounding jungle served as post-operative wards. Within twenty-four hours of our arrival at Tumbru, the ADMS, Brigadier Meneces, visited the unit to discuss the problems, and, as was his custom, got his salute in first. Major Hooper was to hand over the unit and then return to India after there had been a check of equipment and exchange of signatures. Since entering the Arakan, the mobile unit had had to rely upon borrowed transport obtained from any convenient field ambulance or combatant unit. One could hardly sign for the unit's missing trucks, last heard of at Jhansi, and it came as no surprise that the Brigadier did not consider that it would be a good idea for the new O/C of No 7 to accompany Major Hooper back to India to search for the absent vehicles. He ruled that since the unit was actively engaged, it would be best to dispense with the formality of signatures.

Reg Hooper's farewell party was not a great success, as our principal alcoholic stimulant consisted of a limited quantity of luke-warm beer. When the beer was exhausted, the chief guest produced his own original cocktail, made from the absolute alcohol he had salvaged from Maungdaw and flavoured with a choice of melted boiled sweets or passion fruit juice. No one was willing to try out the mixture so its blender, now freed from responsibilities, poured out half a mugful for himself. After a few minutes of animated, if incoherent, conversation, he abruptly fell silent in mid-sentence, passed out and rolled off the camp bed into the scuppers of the tent. We carried him back to his own camp bed and kept him under close observation until he showed signs of coming round, several hours later. The next morning a chastened Major Hooper set off on his journey north, still suffering from a monumental hangover.

At Tumbru, the heat and increasing humidity meant that the skin was constantly moist, and before long prickly heat made for uncomfortable days and sleepless nights. For operations, sterile gowns were used and 'wet gloves' were worn; boiled rubber gloves were placed in a basin of sterile water and the hands were thrust into the water-filled gloves, displacing the fluid as each glove was drawn on. The constant moisture under gloves and gown aggravated the prickly heat, the spots of which coalesced to produce raw forearms. On at least a couple of occasions it was possible to make a trip of a few miles across the neck of the Teknaf peninsula to enjoy the luxury of a palliative saline soak in the tepid waters of the Bay of Bengal. For the unwary, the bathe was marred by treading on a poisonous type of sea urchin which produced a most painful sting; the black spines had to be extracted one by one from the sole of the foot, and the intense pain could be controlled only by injections of local anaesthetic.

The heat certainly suited the flies which were our constant companions, particularly at meal times when they decorated the slices of bully beef and rather dampened the appetite. The British house fly has dark, reddish brown, almost kindly eyes; its Arakan cousin was the size of a bluebottle with light red vicious-looking eyes. The maggots of the house fly eat only dead tissue and it is not generally known that they are recognised as being a most effective agent in cleaning up a necrotic wound in the course of a few days. One hot summer before the war, when I was resident at Cumberland Infirmary, Carlisle, my chief, before going on holiday, had suggested how I should treat an apparently hopeless patient whose nose had been completely replaced by a stinking, fungating cancer. Radium needles were inserted into the growth which was then covered with a Stent plaque carrying more needles and the appliance was stitched in position. Because of the stench, the woman was nursed on the balcony of the ward; in a few days, she began to get restless and the sister in charge asked me to do the dressing as she had seen a maggot crawl out from under the plaque. On exposure of the area, there were seen to be hundreds of juicy maggots filling the nasal openings like melon seeds. After removing the intruders, it was evident that the growth had disappeared. It would seem that as the radium killed off the cancer, the maggots devoured the dead growth and exposed more tumour cells to radiation. The resulting clean, raw area quickly healed, and although the woman left hospital without a nose her cancer had been cured.

Unfortunately, the Burmese maggot does not restrict its diet to dead tissue. The habit was strikingly demonstrated in the case of an Arakan civilian who had sustained a relatively minor gunshot wound of the left forearm. The damaged soft tissues and bone fragments were excised and after applying a protective dressing of vaseline lint, the limb was encased in plaster. The morning after operation, the patient took his own discharge and disappeared back into the jungle. A week later he returned in obvious distress from the hundreds of maggots which were flourishing under his plaster. They had eaten all the skin off his forearm and were feasting on living muscle. There was no alternative but to amputate the arm above the elbow and then retain him until healing was complete. A week later, a soldier was brought in with neglected burns of the thigh; once again the rogue maggots had established themselves to eat living skin and muscle well beyond the burnt area. An extensive excision was required followed by the application of an occlusive dressing which, it was hoped, would keep out the flies during the evacuation to the plastic surgery unit at base hospital.

Whilst on the subject of flies, mention must be made of the so-called mango fly which seemed to flourish during the pre-monsoon time of the year. The mango fly is a minute insect less than quarter the size of a pin's head; a hovering group gave the impression of black spots in front of the eyes. Their unpleasant habit was to try to lay their eggs within the eyelids, the result being a troublesome conjunctivitis which, in some cases, progressed to corneal erosions and permanent impairment of vision. On occasions, a malingerer would try to simulate the effects of infection by the mango fly by putting *dhobi* mark (a dye used to mark clothes) under his lid. A few days of irrigations usually quickly cleared up this self-inflicted injury and prevented the culprit's aim – evacuation back to India.

The heat combined with an inadequate intake of fluid sometimes created problems in patients treated with sulphanilamides. This 'wonder drug' of the early 40's had been discovered in Germany prior to the war; later it had been improved and developed in the UK by the firm of May & Baker. M & B 693 was started post-operatively on a sepoy whose finger had required amputation following a gun-shot wound. By next day, having taken 12 gm of the drug, he passed 30 oz of blood-stained urine. The M & B was stopped, fluids were pushed and a mixture of potassium citrate was given. In spite of this, another 24 hours saw a diminution in the output of blood-stained urine; the patient had no complaint other than an ache in the loins. Next pure blood only was passed and on introducing a catheter, the bladder was found to be empty indicating the the sulphanilamide had crystallised out in the tubules of the kidneys to produce anuria (suppression of the secretion of urine). The mobile surgical unit did not possess a cystoscope which can be used to deal with this complication and so, at Tumbru, other measures had to be tried. Intravenous glucose saline was given and the bladder was distended with boracic lotion. After Glauber salt solution had been introduced into a vein, the excretion of urine restarted. At first there was an increased output for 24 hours, then output became normal and recovery was complete.

No 6 Indian Mobile Surgical Unit had been working east of the Mayo Ridge. Because of the rapid advance of the Japanese, this unit had had to make a hasty withdrawal over the Goppe Pass, leaving their equipment behind. We had fleeting visits from their Indian surgeon and British anaesthetist making their separate ways northwards. One gained the impression that the Japs were hard on their heels and soon would reach Tumbru, but the only Jap to arrive was a wounded prisoner who was under constant guard. At this stage of the war, live Japanese prisoners were hard to come by as it was their custom to commit suicide to avoid capture. This particular prisoner, Superior Private Atsumura Ichiro, had sustained a gunshot wound of the right leg. Harikari had been prevented and there was an additional bonus in that the intelligence officer, Major Miller, had previously been able to obtain from the man seemingly important information for which confirmation was required. The patient needed an anaesthetic to have his wound dealt with and so, with Major Miller in attendance, George Quayle gave a small dose of Pentothal and then allowed the man to surface sufficiently to answer the questions once again. The Jap, under the influence of the 'truth drug' confirmed his previous statements and named the location of the Japanese Divisional Headquarters. At this point, the intelligence officer left the theatre to pass on the information by field telephone; the anaesthetic was deepened to allow for the operation to be carried out and the limb was encased in plaster. By the time the patient was being carried from the theatre *basha* to the post-operative tent in the bushes, a squadron of RAF bombers passed low overhead bound for the south. We never heard whether or not they found and bombed this particular target.

But this time the trickle of wounded was reaching the unit in a bad way after a hard, hot journey lasting up to a couple of days, so preparations were made for a possible move forward. Equipment sufficient to deal with fifty cases was distributed into panniers, to make thirty-one mule loads. But no sooner was this expedition ready to set off than the cancellation order came, since gathering clouds indicated that the onset of the monsoon proper would not be long delayed. On another visit, Brigadier Meneces advised us that, in view of the impending moves, it would be desirable to reduce our personal kit; so, after sorting out and repacking, my precious tin trunk was evacuated to Grindley's Bank in Calcutta, where it remained for the next eighteen months.

As May advanced, heat and humidity increased. My own living conditions were somewhat eased by a move from the 40 lb tent to share with George Quayle a newly constructed *basha* on the top of one of the surrounding hills. Here the Turkish-bath type of heat was occasionally diminished by the slight breeze wafting from the west. From the balcony of the *basha* there was a hazy view of the blue Mayo Ridge, some twenty miles away to the south-east. In the other direction the dusty road north could be seen, passing between paddy fields to disappear into thick foliage a mile away. In case we might have to remain for a longer period at Tumbru, some pre-monsoon preparations were made. From the engineers at Tumbru Ghat it was possible to beg a few bags of cement and give the theatre floor a smooth, hard covering. Boards were laid between the theatre *basha* and the post-operative tents; the surrounds of the tents were banked up with sand bags and drainage gulleys were dug.

During the night of 27th May, a severe and spectacular thunderstorm ushered in the real monsoon. The rain beat down with terrific violence and, apart from short breaks, continued incessantly for days and nights. The intermittent lulls in the downpour held a certain fascination; it seemed as if the drawing across the sky of a giant zip fastener suddenly cut off the flow and then, in perhaps an hour, the zip would be opened to allow the abrupt resumption of the barrage with renewed fury. Unfortunately, the sudden onset of the monsoon caught the Unit before all its preparations were completed and whole supplies of sugar, flour and cement were washed away.

Once the monsoon was established, flies disappeared but humidity increased and this produced a worsening of skin irritation from prickly heat. In the open, the choice lay between the wearing of no protection and getting soaked or covering up with a ground sheet which aggravated the prickly heat. The hitherto dusty compound was transformed into a muddy lake and the theatre *basha* had to be reached across duck-boards. The main supply route from the north was frequently blocked by landfalls, floods and broken bridges, but from the south communications were kept open along the Naf and its tributaries. During the weeks that followed, the unit continued to cope with casualties which were arriving in decreasing numbers after appalling journeys; once the wounded had been operated on, their evacuation north was an ordeal which some did not survive.

Soon after the rains came, we had a couple of long operating lists mainly grenade and mortar-shell casualties. Many of these men reached Tumbru soaked and shivering after a rough trip lasting several days. Amongst the admissions was a critically ill, semi-conscious sepoy from whom no history could be obtained. He had a tender swelling occupying the lower right side of the abdomen, at first sight strongly suggestive of an appendix abscess. More careful examination revealed a minute puncture wound in the right buttock. At operation, it was found that he had a localised infected collection of blood just where an appendix abscess would have formed. A mortar-shell fragment the size of a split-pea had gone right through the pelvic bone to damage the back of the caecum (large bowel). After drainage of the abscess and removal of the fragment, he made a slow but complete recovery. This patient was one of the first to demonstrate to me that intra-abdominal damage must be considered as a possibility even although a small entry wound is apparently well clear of the abdomen.

It became increasingly evident that the only remaining surgical unit in the Arakan would need to move nearer to the scene of activities. At the end of June, it came as no surprise to receive the movement order for No 7 to advance to join a field ambulance at Bawli Bazar.

CHAPTER FIVE

Glorious Mud

Once the monsoon began in earnest, all military activity in the area came to an enforced halt. The Japanese were firmly established along the line of the Maungdaw-Buthidaung road and the district to the north of this was given over to spasmodic patrolling from both sides. The resulting casualties were limited, but men picked up from the mud and rain had a long, rough journey ahead before they could receive surgical attention. Bearer units would take the wounded for first aid measures to the MDS (Main Dressing Station) of the Field Ambulance at Bawli Bazar. Further evacuation to reach No 7 was uncertain involving a trek of fourteen miles over rough jungle road along which bridge repairs were frequently necessary. The alternative route was by river steamer, down the Pruma and then up the Naf to Tumbru Ghat.

At the time of the proposed forward move, we were informed that the Tumbru-Bawli road had been blocked in several places and it might be a week before truck transport would be able to get through. Our previous organisation, getting equipment down to mule loads, could not now be used, as at this time no mules were available at Tumbru. The only way was to use river transport, and the unit began its preparations for the first step down the road to Tumbru Ghat.

Before our packing had been completed, we had to unpack and re-open the theatre to deal with a couple of Indians who had sustained unusual neck wounds. In each instance, the patient had escaped death by a hair's breadth. The first sepoy, who had been hit in the neck by a Jap rifle bullet, was brought in a couple of hours after sustaining the wound. On removing the temporary field dressing, the right side of the neck was seen to be tense, discoloured and swollen to the size of a large grapefruit; in the centre of the swelling there was a small entry wound from which partially clotted blood was oozing. At the back of the neck towards the right, a larger exit wound had ceased bleeding. At operation, the large haematoma was opened up and the blood clot cleaned away; it quickly became evident that free venous bleeding was issuing from a torn internal jugular vein; in order to control the loss of blood, division of the large vein was completed and both ends were tied off. It was then possible to assess the situation and see that the carotid arteries, important nerves, the larynx and the cervical spine had all escaped injury.

The second sepoy, whilst on patrol, had demanded from his section leader that he be allowed to fall out for rest and refreshment. An Indian NCO told him that they must continue until it was safe to halt. The sepoy then strongly asserted that, unless he was allowed to have a break, he would shoot himself. The Havildar, not taking the threat seriously, told him to get on with it; whereupon the man put his rifle to the left upper part of his neck and pulled the trigger. The bullet passed through the salivary gland and out through the mouth without touching the great vessels or shattering the jaw. When the entry wound was opened up and the bloodclot evacuated, it was found that the vessels to and from the salivary gland were the only ones requiring ligature. The incident put the patient off his curry and rice for no more than a few days.

A couple of miles from the Field Ambulance at Tumbru, on a backwater of the River Naf, was the Ghat. It consisted of fifty dreary yards of timbered quay, supporting a single rusty crane, a litter of hawsers and piles of packing cases. Groups of bamboo storage huts huddled forlornly in the dark mass of the jungle which relentlessly pushed itself back in its ceaseless, purposeful reclamation of the clearing. Groves of mangrove trees stretched out from the ends of the jetty into the black, stinking mud of the estuary, the whole depressing scene barely visible through the curtain of the persisting deluge.

We had to make several trips along the treacherously muddy road in order to convey the unit and its equipment to the Ghat in borrowed trucks. Then through the grey rain, we sighted the river steamer *Elsa*. Cautiously, she eased alongside the quay and was made secure, the tricky manoeuvre made more difficult by the fact that wooden sloops had been bound to either side of the craft to increase her carrying capacity. Our equipment was passed across the first sloop and then over the steamer into the hold of the second. Stores and ammunition were then loaded into the main holds until all three vessels lay low in the water. The personnel of No 7 then settled on board *Elsa* which sailed at 1500 hours.

For many decades before the war, *Elsa* must have seen constant service on the tidal waters of the Naf and its tributaries. The Japanese occupation of Maungdaw had blocked the mouth of the estuary but, even had she reached the Bay of Bengal, it seemed doubtful whether her rusty plates would have stood the buffeting of the open sea. Trapped in the upper reaches, *Elsa* remained to give valuable service. When the main road was impassable, she was the only means of supply to the forward troops and on her return journeys she became a hospital ship for the evacuation of the wounded to Tumbru Ghat. The external appearance of senility was matched by the state of her engines, which were in no condition to battle with the Pruma in spate.

It soon became evident that the addition of two sloops was too much of a load for progress to be made upstream, so on reaching the confluence of the Naf and the Pruma, a turnabout had to be made, to be followed by a slow crawl back to Tumbru Ghat, keeping away from the main force of the river. Engine repairs occupied the next twenty-four hours and during this time the unit had to disembark, in order to be accommodated back at the Field Ambulance. The night of 29th June we spent on board, in company with cockroaches and rats. For our next venture, one sloop was left behind and when *Elsa* again made her way downstream, her engines sounded in a better state of health. The constant downpour limited our visibility but also prevented any attention from enemy aircraft. After chugging for an hour along the western shore of the Teknaf peninsula, a U-turn was made from the Naf into the Pruma and the mangrove swamps were left behind. On this occasion, the serviced engines were able to maintain a slow but steady progress upstream towards Bawli Bazar. In another four hours we reached our destination and at a small wooden jetty on the north bank of the Pruma, *Elsa* relieved herself of the sloop and then moved on alone for a further mile to discharge her military cargo just below Bawli bridge.

From the jetty, a partially bricked, raised track passed between flooded paddy fields to reach a collection of bamboo huts which represented the Main Dressing Station of No 66 Field Ambulance We spent that morning unloading the sloop and transferring equipment to shelter beside the largest hut, which had been used by the Field Ambulance for dressings and needed some modification to convert it into an operating theatre. Early the next morning it was in use to deal with a civilian Moghul Ahmed whose chest had been opened by a Japanese bullet. It is unlikely that he would have survived if the operation to close the sucking wound had had to be delayed until he reached Tumbru, at least a day's journey away from Bawli.

Soon after our arrival, I was required to attend headquarters a few miles away north of Bawli bridge. Truck transport was not on, nor was the alternative of wading on foot through stretches of deep mud. A horse was provided for the trip and although lacking any previous equestrian experience, I boldly mounted and set off. I considered myself fortunate that the animal could only make very slow progress, as it cautiously plodded its way through mud and water which often reached halfway up its legs. At one point a narrow sloping track skirted a slimy pool from which protruded the body of a fully laden mule which obviously had failed to keep its feet on this particular section. I clung more tightly as the horse, no doubt well aware of the danger, step by step, gradually picked its way past this difficult spot.

On the higher ground, the deep mud lessened and I began to feel more confident until, on rounding a bend, the Indian personnel of an ack-ack battery turned out to salute the lone rider. In returning the salute, I lost my already precarious balance and only restored the situation by encircling the horse's neck with both arms. No doubt the men of the battery took a poor view of my riding ability, but it would have been even more humiliating if they had had to fish me out of the mire. The journey back from headquarters was equally harrowing, as failing light was added to the downpour, the mud and my uncertain powers of horsemanship.

At the Field Ambulance, accommodation at first was in banked-up 40 lb tents and later in *bashas* dotted between the small hillocks. Meals were taken in a 120 lb tent protected by sandbags and surrounded by gulleys to carry away the excess of water. Since the monsoon had put a damper on any major contacts with the enemy, the casualties at this time, came mainly from patrol encounters. No 7 settled into what was to be its home for the next six months. Living conditions were improved by the siting of the mess in a large *basha* on the top of a hillock and by the provision of small single *bashas* above swamp level.

Craftsmen, without using a single nail, put up these dwellings at surprising speed. The floor of interlaced strips of bamboo was laid on bamboo stilts to clear the surface of the mud. Meantime, the walls were being woven by native women whose menfolk used creeper thongs to fix these walls in position. Finally there was added the thick roof made from elephant grass held by crossed strips of bamboo. An opening on one wall was left as a window which could be closed by sliding across it a woven square, carried on bamboo runners. An ever-open door was provided for the entrance to the basha. Next to the entrance steps, a few square yards of bamboo flooring, neatly screened, created a bathroom. The final result of a couple of days of labouring, was a *basha* which was generally leakproof during the monsoon and at other times afforded good protection from the afternoon sun.

The interior of the *basha* was furnished with a chair, a table and a camp bed, draped with a mosquito net and sited beside the window space. The mosquito net, apart from its intended purpose, gave a sense of security. Before retiring, everyone would make sure that no snakes, millipedes or other livestock lurked in the bed. Thereafter, the net gave protection from anything that might drop from the roof. On one occasion, the intruder was a wild cat which screeched furiously on becoming caught in the top of the netting from which it was with difficulty eventually disentangled to the accompaniment of much cursing, clawing and biting.

One early morning, in the dark hours, I was awakened by the sound of heavy breathing beside the door opening. It was not possible to see the creature and I lay still behind the mosquito netting, not even moving to take my revolver from under the pillow. Another pause was followed by a series of deep grunts before it slipped back into the jungle. I wondered if the night visitor had been a water buffalo, but on inspection by daylight, there, clearly visible, I found the pug marks of a fully grown tiger. After this experience, door and window apertures were blocked for at least a couple of nights, but heat and humidity led to their re-opening.

The larger animals usually made themselves scarce, but problems did arise at times. There was an occasion when the medical officer of a Field Ambulance found that his patients had been performing their natural functions on the floor beside their beds. He proceeded to deliver a full-blooded telling off and asked why the lazy, dirty buggers had not used the nearby latrines. He was greeted with cries of:

'*Sahib, bahut tacklif* (much trouble), tiger in latrines!'

He told them not to be so stupid and in order to put their minds at rest, boldly went round to the latrines, where he did indeed come face to face with a large tiger! Both MO and tiger hastily left the latrines at opposite ends!

No wild elephants ventured near Bawli Bazar, but from the Teknaf peninsula the remains of a soldier was brought to the Unit after an unfortunate encounter. It seems that a few men, inexperienced in stalking elephant, had set out on a hunt. Although the animal had been hit in the head with a Sten gun bullet, its advance had not been halted and it trampled to death the would-be big game hunter.

The small carnivora, jackal and hyena, in addition to punctuating the night with their calls, caused problems because of their habit of raiding fresh graves. In order to discourage this, deeper graves were dug and the blanket-wrapped corpse was surrounded by wire netting before burial. Although playing an important role as a scavenger, an even more disgusting creature was the vulture with its habit of extracting the entrails of man and beast; for this purpose, the long featherless neck was thrust through the anus into the cadaver's abdomen. At times, groups of vultures would settle on the surrounds of the Field Ambulance and, for morale's sake, it was considered desirable to move them on with the aid of a Tommy gun; although bullets could be seen scattering feathers as the birds ponderously took off, not one vulture ever failed to become airborne and make its escape.

Apart from necessitating elementary precautions, particularly when converting an old *basha* into an operating theatre, snakes did not present any serious problems. There were official instructions that if a person received a snake bite, the head of the reptile was to be examined to identify its variety and so decide upon the type of anti-venom serum to be used in the treatment. Only one member of the unit was bitten and, as it turned out, the snake had not been of a poisonous type; in any case, identification of the variety was not possible as the head of the reptile had been beaten to pulp before the incident was reported. In the wet season particularly, the evening dip in the canvas bath located in the 'bathroom' just outside the *basha*, provided evidence of snake activity. One could hear nearby loud croakings which, on investigation, were found to be issuing from partially swallowed frogs; those frogs, taken by the hind legs, certainly made loud protests before they disappeared down the snake's gullet.

The only evidence that pythons inhabited the jungle near Bawli was brought to our notice one morning when a dead specimen was delivered at the Field Ambulance for inspection. The large reptile had made the fatal mistake of managing to swallow a small goat whose horns could not be accommodated and had perforated the python's flank. From the Field Ambulance, a would-be taxidermist, acquired the specimen for a few rupees, in the hope that in due course he would be able to provide shoes and handbags for all his female relations; unfortunately his 'do-it-yourself' efforts at curing were far from satisfactory and before long the stinking remains had to be buried.

The author's *basha* at Bawli Bazar

CHAPTER SIX

The Other Enemy

In the first Arakan campaign, enemy No 1 was the mosquito. This insect, the carrier of the malarial parasite, had been responsible for more casualties than the Japanese, until by early 1943 for every soldier entering Burma, two had to be invalided back with malaria. During the long, arduous evacuation, it was common for re-infection to occur; once the patient had reached India, it was not infrequent for months to pass before his recurrent malaria could be controlled and in many instances the man was never fit enough to return to Burma. Before a successful offensive could be launched against the Japanese, it was essential to overcome this loss of manpower.

In late 1943 and early 1944, by using insecticides to spray the stagnant pools which were the breeding grounds for the mosquito, by enforcing strict anti-malarial discipline and by providing mepacrine, the disease was successfully defied. If the records showed that the incidence of malaria was unduly high in any unit, the commanding officer was held responsible and be liable to be relieved of his command. In addition to issuing the orders, he had to ensure that they were properly carried out. Camp beds had to be protected by adequate netting and before dusk, shorts were to be replaced by long trousers tucked into the boots. At night it was recommended that any exposed skin should be covered with insect repellent cream and whenever possible, netting was to be draped over the bush hat. An additional important measure was the provision of MFTU's (Malarial Forward Treatment Units); these centres in *bashas* or tents a few miles behind the fighting lines, enabled the disease to be treated in its early stage and brought a cure within a few weeks. The soldier could be quickly returned to his unit and the strain on the difficult lines of communication was greatly reduced.

In the earlier part of 1943 when morale was low, some men took no precautions to avoid malaria; they welcomed the disease which could get them back to India and away from the terrors of the jungle. The MFTU's showed such men that a bout of malaria was not so attractive when it removed them no more than a few miles from the front and then speedily returned them to their units.

Mepacrine which was a most important factor in the control of malaria had to be taken regularly in order to be effective. To ensure this, each morning No 7 was on parade, mouths were opened, a tablet was placed on the tongue and the order given to swallow; a check was then made to make sure that the mepacrine had been swallowed. As a result of this, combined with the other precautions, not a single member of No 7 Indian Mobile Surgical Unit succumbed to malaria. After many months on Mepacrine, the British personnel developed a yellowish tinge to the skin and this raised the question of possible liver damage. Captain McMartin, a biochemist and pathologist, undertook forward investigations into this problem and failed to find any evidence of harmful effects from the prolonged use of the drug. The Japanese who were no less susceptible to the malarial parasite than anyone else, realising the importance of the role played by Mepacrine in keeping troops in action and themselves not having any such effective alternative, put out propaganda that the drug caused impotence. This false allegation failed to make any impression on malarial prophylaxis and some troops for themselves proved the fallacy by acquiring various types of venereal disease in Calcutta during their leaves!

In Arakan, from the surgical aspect, it was necessary always to be aware of the spectre of malaria lurking in the background. When presented with a suspected acute abdomen, one considered the possibility of malaria before that of appendicitis. We felt certain that wounds and operations could produce a flare-up of dormant malaria. Although at this time this opinion was not accepted by the Lethbridge Commission on Malaria, as a routine we continued to add quinine in post-operative drips and with its use, rigors and high fevers ceased to be post-operational features. Recurrent attacks of malaria in due course produced secondary anaemia; at operation, compensation was required for this anaemia by giving blood, even in those cases when in civil life transfusion would not normally have been required. Another point which had to be considered was that a patient with uncorrected anaemia would be more liable to develop infective complications and therefore the healing of wounds could be delayed. A surgical manifestation of malaria, encountered more often in the chronically infected Burmese and Indians, was the considerably enlarged friable spleen, which was liable to rupture from even a relatively minor blow on the abdomen; several such patients came our way with internal haemorrhage for which urgent removal of the spleen was required.

In Europe, the venereologist would understand 'Full House' not as a poker term but as referring to a patient who had acquired both syphilis and gonorrhoea. Out East, however, the phrase could be taken to mean that the patient had, without any special skill, picked up syphilis, gonorrhoea, lymphogranuloma and soft chancre all at one session; the simultaneous combination of these four diseases certainly presented diagnostic problems. It was realised that in Calcutta some troops made a point of deliberately acquiring gonorrhoea at least. After five days of incubation, just the time taken for a man to reach the front line, the urethral discharge had developed and he would be ready and more than willing for evacuation back to India. But by 1943–44, just as in the case of malaria, these patients were held in Burma and treated in forward specialised units.

Scrub typhus, which was particularly troublesome on the Burmese northern front, rarely showed itself in Arakan. At times, the physicians of the Field Ambulance had to cope with sporadic infective cases which could be lethal. On one occasion, a native was brought in from Bawli with confluent smallpox, the eruption completely covering the skin surface; he was nursed in a small tent on the paddy field beside the Pruma but failed to survive, despite intensive medical treatment. This single case led to a widespread re-vaccination of all personnel. At a later date, early one morning, a sepoy was admitted to the isolation basha soon after developing symptoms and signs of cholera. Drugs and intravenous fluids failed to control the rapidly advancing toxaemia and dehydration produced by the disease, with its constant bloody diarrhoea. By sundown the man was dead and buried. The *basha* was burnt and a large scale anti-cholera inoculation was instituted. These potentially devastating infections could crop up at any time amongst the native population; no doubt strict hygienic measures and inoculations prevented the development of these diseases in epidemic form amongst the military personnel.

Parasitic infestations, other than malaria, did not make any real impact on the troops but there was no doubt that intestinal worms tended to produce a lowering of morale, anaemia and a general feeling of ill-health. After an anaesthetic, it was common in Indian troops to have large collections of round worms in the post-operative vomitus. Sometimes, during operations for intestinal injuries, clumps of worms appeared at the site of the bowel laceration and required removal before repairing the damage. The effect of the guinea worm was only seen in those Indians and Arakanese who favoured bare feet, the usual site of entry for the parasite. This worm inhabits the connective tissues of the body and the female, when mature, pushes her head to a skin surface in search of water into which the embryos are ejected. The usual site for pointing is in the lower leg and here a blister may form. The man himself invariably was familiar with the condition and often he had started the process of extraction; the worm's head was attached to a matchstick on to which it was gradually wound day by day and eventually a specimen many feet in length might be produced. Surgical attention was only sought for those who broke the worm or if cellulitis and abscesses developed.

The scorpion had to be avoided as the possible source of a painful sting, but most men managed to steer clear of this creature. Each morning, everyone as a routine made sure that nothing lurked in his boots. Some blood sport enthusiasts made a point of capturing scorpions and staging contests in the style of cock-fighting. After these battles, both victor and vanquished met the same fate.

The leech was common in the Arakan and it was not unusual any evening to spot several such creatures looping their way across the matting of the *basha*, looking for food. They could attach themselves to the skin unnoticed and the host would only become aware that he was providing a free meal when he observed the engorged, dark red leech hanging from his skin. Such an attachment was easily broken by applying the end of a lighted cigarette to the tail of the parasite which immediately let go its hold and dropped off. These pests had the remarkable ability of allowing nothing to stand in their way in their search for nourishment. Troops on patrol found that leeches could reach the feet through lace holes in their boots and the man would only notice this penetration when, on removing his boots, he found his feet soaked in blood. One unusual example presented at the unit; a leech had attached itself to a man's tonsil, thus demonstrating one of the disadvantages of sleeping with the mouth open.

Whilst on the subject of leeches, it seems worth mentioning an incident which took place hundreds of miles away from Arakan. Early in 1945, my leave had been arranged in company with Major William Weston who, a year previously, had brought No 15 Indian Mobile Surgical Unit to join No 7 at Zeganbyn. Bill Weston had fixed up for our leave to be spent with a missionary relative, the Reverend Arthur Rumpus, who, for many years, had been trying, with little success, to make converts at Kodaikanal, in the hill country of South India. We were to spend a fortnight's holiday at the missionary's house, in a delightful climate resembling that of Scotland on a warm summer's day. Our headaches, the result of the change to the high altitude, settled in a couple of days and we were ready for the special treat of a trip to Lake Perriare, where elephants had been seen swimming, and along the shores of which, so it had been reported tigers had been chased by packs of wild dogs.

We made the journey from Kodaikanal by bus, down a twisting road with many hairpin bends, which left the level of the pine trees to wend its way through the tea plantations, past the banana belt and finally through light jungle to the red, arid plain of Travencore; the trip then continued for many dusty miles towards the forest of Perriare. At one of the village halts we saw, amongst the children who came crowding around the bus, what at first appeared to be a fair-haired European boy. He wore ragged Indian garments and when we noticed that he used his hands to protect his eyes from the bright sun, we realised that he was an albino. Perhaps it should be explained that, although born of Indian parents, some congenital defect had deprived this boy of all pigmentation, including that protecting the retinae of his eyes.

In the late afternoon, we transferred to a light truck to continue on our way into jungle of increasing density and eventually at dusk, settled into a wooden guest hut which accommodated us for the night. Next morning Bill Weston, who was a keen bird-watcher, wished to explore the nearby forest in the hope that he might catch sight of the racket-tailed drongo. This rare bird was rather like a blackbird with a long forked tail, the ends of which were extended to terminate in a couple of feathery tufts. Bill never saw the racket-tailed drongo, but whilst on the lake next morning, we were both impressed by the sound and sight of the greater hornbill. It is an exceptionally large bird, some four feet in length, and we heard it in flight for near on a mile, because the noisy thrashing of its great wings gave the impression that it was some mechanical aircraft rather than one of nature's grotesques.

Bill was loth to abandon the search for the drongo, and soon we, accompanied by bearers carrying elephant guns, had penetrated the forest. Here we were interested to observe that the huts of a small village were set well above the ground level, being located around the first tree-fork and reached by a type of rope ladder. It was at this point we noticed that our bearers had developed red ankles and then we realised why the natives lived up in the trees. Although we were wearing battle dress tucked into mosquito boots, the leeches, in scores, had found their way to the skin of our legs and thighs, the highest attachment being just below the groins. We dashed back to a clearing and quickly removed our nether garments to pull off the swollen leeches; there was no time to indulge in the more refined method of applying the end of a lighted cigarette. Bill enlivened the de-leeching process by giving a loud, prolonged selection of most lurid cursing, the profanities ceasing only when he caught sight of the aghast missionary. Then, without batting an eyelid, he came out with:

'I'm so sorry, Arthur. Please excuse my bad language; it is the result of my prolonged association with the rough and rude soldiery!'

Because we had pulled off the leeches, the heads were left attached in the skin and the anti-coagulant secretions continued to act. Even by the next day, circles of blood continued to seep through our trousers. This was noticed by the Indian forester who took us on the lake in his boat; he promptly grounded the boat and, after a short search, produced a green plant. He told us to crush the leaves and apply them to the leech bites; within a couple of minutes all oozing had ceased and it did not recur. It would be interesting to know what powerful coagulant factor was in this plant, which grew so conveniently near the leech forest of Perriare.

In Burma, in spite of a somewhat primitive daily bath and a crew-cut hair style, it was difficult to keep clear of various skin troubles. In addition to prickly heat, which has already been mentioned, fungus infections tended to thrive, especially during the hot, moist times of the year. Some produced no actual disease, one example being a dark red growth of fungus which proliferated in the hair of the armpits and pubic region without any apparent harmful effect. It was of interest and relief to note that pre-monsoon prickly heat gave little trouble when the second monsoon approached; by this time the skin had become acclimatised to the conditions, thanks to the development of a good sun tan above the waist.

At all times, there flourished the fungus responsible for the so-called '*Dhobi*'s Itch'. It was not uncommon to have a soldier complaining bitterly about this condition, for which he was asking to be put on light duties; before ordering treatment with gentian violet, it gave me a little satisfaction to draw up the legs of my shorts to show him my own groins which were in a rather worse state than his. The most painful fungus infection was that involving the ear external to the drum, and this could mean many sleepless nights before frequent packing with medicated gauze eventually controlled the condition.

In addition to the fungal attacks, the skin was subject to other infections which could be equally as troublesome; on bare legs any small cut or abrasion, perhaps sustained from a splinter of bamboo, frequently developed a chronic diphtheroid infection which produced ulcers persisting for many weeks in spite of treatment. (I still have the scars to prove it!)

Quite apart from the production of skin ailments, fungi made their presence felt in other directions; those officers who ignored the instruction that cameras should not be taken into Burma came to regret their disobedience. One captain, almost in tears, showed me the remains of his expensive camera, which had failed to survive the ravages of heat, humidity and fungal infection; the bellows of the camera had fallen apart and the greenish fungus on the leather had completed the spoiling process.

It might be assumed that, in Arakan, all nature combined to make life unpleasant, but this was not entirely so. The attractive chameleons, the great variety of lizards and the noisy frogs all waged their war on the insect population. In the mess *basha* we had a resident lizard of large proportions; he attached himself to the bamboo rafters and entertained us at meal times. He would remain motionless for long periods and then there would be a sudden grab, followed by the noisy crunching up of some large moth. Another creature not particularly shy of humans was the tree rat; this animal resembled a grey squirrel, except for several black and white lines passing down the back onto the tail. Tree rats did not hesitate to pay a visit to collect delicacies, soap, other than carbolic, being a great favourite. Once, after an operating session, I had to wash out my blood-stained khaki shorts and hung them to dry beside the entrance to the *basha*. By the next morning, it was obvious that my laundering had not been completely successful; these rodents had moved in and eaten away every portion of fabric retaining the slightest flavour of blood.

When the monsoon eased, the hillsides became alive with huge, gorgeous butterflies, some swallow tailed, others striped and all of iridescent colours. In order to collect some specimens during a quiet period, we fashioned butterfly nets from bamboo, wire and mosquito netting. One morning, an unexpected visit from a general coincided with the unit's butterfly hunt. We feared that he might have some uncomplimentary remarks to make at such a sight, but not so; he was a keen entomologist who, during the meal and afterwards, discussed butterflies at great length, instructing us in methods of killing, preserving, fixing and packing specimens for transmission home.

Apart from bombers, fighters and vultures, aerial activity could be quite entertaining. On hot evenings, a slight noise would disturb the calm and from the mango groves large droves of ponderously

On leave at Kodaikanal

flapping fruit bats would fill the sky before finding another resting place. At other times, hundreds of vivid green and blue parakeets would circle round and round our camp, then re-settle in the trees to resume their chattering. During the pre and post-monsoon months, dawns and sunsets presented memorable pictures; the orange, rose and crimson tints of the thunder clouds over the Mayo Ridge were backed by a cobalt blue sky shading to deep purple. This glory of the heavens was accentuated by the dark greens of the jungle. It was unfortunate that we were never allowed to forget the war for very long as the sound of a rifle shot or a fierce yammering of a machine gun would shatter the idyllic scene, jerking us back to reality.

CHAPTER SEVEN

Who Needs Enemies?

After the full force of the monsoon eased, activity increased south of the river, giving an irregular flow of casualties to the unit. Occasionally an order would be received to evacuate all beds and be ready to cope with large numbers of wounded, but no wounded arrived. At other times, when there was no forewarning of any action, floods of casualties came in.

Quite apart from the steady work provided by the enemy, periodically there arrived men with accidental or self-inflicted injuries, many of which should never have happened. In Teknaf, there occurred the tragic meeting of two friends due for repatriation. At a mutual challenge, both demonstrated the speed with which they could draw their weapons. One man's gun went off and the bullet hit his pal in the lower left chest. The patient, whose legs were paralysed, reached us some four hours after the accident. He was cold and clammy, the pulse was rapid and the temperature elevated. In spite of the evidence of gross internal injury, the blood pressure was unexpectedly high; the explanation for this was found at operation. In its passage through lung, diaphragm, stomach, kidney and lower thoracic spine, the bullet had caused marked bleeding in the region of the solar plexus. The collection of blood in this area had been responsible, by stimulating the nerves, for the uncharacteristic blood pressure recording. In spite of transfusion, once the abdomen was opened and the tension relieved, there was a sudden collapse with the pressure becoming unrecordable. Intense resuscitation was continued after operation without avail and the man died several hours later.

The Sten gun produced more than its share of accidental wounds; this weapon, unless handled with care, could be bumped into automatic firing, the resulting wounds often involving the buttocks. Booby traps, set in anticipation of Japanese raids and then forgotten, provided several casualties with grenade wounds; a man who had ingeniously fixed a branch to a grenade pin in order to protect the approach to his tent in the bushes, could through some lapse fall a victim himself.

Although at the time of the monsoons, the heavens were often rent with violent thunderstorms, it was surprising how infrequently these electrical discharges produced any direct injury to personnel on the ground. On one occasion, a blinding flash and immediate clap of thunder shook the roof of the company office *basha*. Some fifty yards away we found that the lightning had struck a stationary jeep; the driver, who had had his hand on the windscreen, was killed; his hand had been charred and his skin showed typical aboreal markings. A colleague standing some twenty yards away was in an apathetic state with cold skin, rapid pulse and low blood pressure which soon responded to simple resuscitative measures.

The unpredictable mule was at times responsible for the odd casualty with fractured ribs. Once a sepoy, in a collapsed state from shock, was brought in by ambulance; examination failed to reveal any sign of external or internal injury and after a warm drink he quickly recovered to admit that when the mule maliciously lashed out with its hind legs, the hooves had just touched the man's jacket. This was another example of a near miss producing a nerve-shattering effect. Primary shock certainly responds quickly to a warm drink but in cases of secondary shock from wounds, the patient should only have the fluid supplied intravenously. After having sucked out many gallons of sweet weak tea from the peritoneal cavity, eventually we were able to persuade forward units that those men with abdominal wounds should not be given anything by mouth prior to transference to a surgical unit.

From time to time, particularly when Japanese activity was in abeyance, the unit had to deal with several would-be suicides. The man who shot himself through the head was either dead on arrival or survived no more than a few hours. On the other hand, there was one officer who aimed his revolver just below the left nipple, intending to shoot himself through the heart; the bullet missed its target and, having hit a rib, was deflected round the chest cage to lodge in the right axilla. After excising the entry wound and removing the bullet from the armpit, from the surgical point of view, convalescence was uneventful. In failed suicides, it was usually found that there had been some domestic trouble back home. The attempt could be precipitated by the arrival of a letter from the UK; at the time of its receipt, the man was generally unoccupied and his morale was already in a low state.

Some were more fortunate with their domestic problems. There was an officer who was given his three weeks' leave from Burma. He travelled back to Calcutta and immediately got a flight across India to Karachi. Here he managed to contact friends in the RAF and through them secretly got a lift back to England, where he met his wife and spent a week, mostly in bed, in a London hotel. He recuperated on his flight back to India and rejoined his unit within the time allotted for his leave.

The secret was kept even from his closest friends and after some ten months, when the escapade was no more than a happy memory, he received an urgent call from his commanding officer. The expected confrontation did not materialise and he was treated with tact and sympathy. The O/C had just received from the village vicar a letter in which it was suggested that the news of the wife's recent confinement should be broken gently to 'this poor man, who had been out east during the past three years'. The kindly colonel, after expressing his sorrow, insisted that the officer should take a month's compassionate leave to return home and attempt to sort out the domestic problem. The man concerned, without any change of expression, gratefully accepted the offer and in due course celebrated the unexpected re-union by further increasing the size of his family.

One non-sporting method of obtaining a variation in diet was to get fresh fish from the Pruma without using nets or lines. Usually a grenade was tossed into the river and after this depth charge had exploded, a selection of fish floated to the surface, ready to be collected. A lieutenant of the 2nd KOSB's was an explosive expert and decided to employ his own more powerful charge to increase the yield for his mess. The gelignite exploded before he could toss the bundle into the river and the results were appalling. He was brought to us with multiple injuries which included loss of the right hand, blindness, deafness, blast injury to the chest and abdomen together with skin loss from thighs, penis and scrotum. After operation, the patient was given full-time special care by one of the nursing orderlies loaned from the Field Ambulance. This orderly was a small rustic man who, before the war, had been a farm worker familiar with the care of animals; he had developed into a skilled and dedicated nurse. But in spite of all his attention and devoted care, the patient died a week after receiving his injuries. The orderly had accompanied him on the first stage of the evacuation to Tumbru, where death took place; he was weeping when he returned to report that his efforts had been in vain.

Some wounds were obviously self-inflicted, but in others there was an element of doubt. A soldier with a powder-stained wound on the palm of the hand would insist that he had sustained the injury in close fighting when he had grappled with a Jap's rifle. In some instances it was not possible to dispute this story. If such a patient was evacuated back to India, by the time he reached base hospital he would have flexed, fixed fingers on a useless hand. To counter this development, it was the policy to amputate the involved finger along with its metacarpal and whilst retaining the man in the forward area, concentrate on maintaining full movement of the remaining fingers. This method made it possible to arrange for an early return to his unit of both the keen and the less keen soldier; the latter would soon realise that he had failed in his attempt to 'work his ticket'.

A lieutenant in the RAMC had called to stay the night with the Field Ambulance on his way to join a bearer unit on the eastern side of the Mayo Ridge. He was in a somewhat nervous state when he set out next morning, bound first for the Goppe Pass. By early evening, he was carried back with a bullet wound through the foot. He said that on his way up the pass, he had stopped to open his bowels; whilst squatting, he heard movements in the jungle lower down and then a bullet hit him through the sole of the foot. Unfortunately, at operation, this story could not be substantiated. Although there were no powder stains around either entry or exit wounds, at excision it was found that pieces of skin had been driven into the surface of the lower tibia indicating that the bullet had passed from above downwards. A later discovery was the powder-stained jacket through which the revolver had been fired. The patient was, after a few days, evacuated to face a court martial. No doubt the defence would question how it came about that a young, inexperienced officer, within a week of landing at Bombay and without having had some opportunity to become adjusted, found himself exposed on his own to the terrors of the Burmese jungle.

On two separate occasions, 'friendly' air strikes were responsible for a considerable amount of havoc. In the spring of 1944, a large force of Liberators, seeking the Razabil fortress, scattered their bombs far and wide so providing a stream of civilian casualties requiring the attention of No 7. Before this, an even worse accident made 7th August 1943, a very black day. On the paddy field near the jetty projecting into the Pruma, the Field Ambulance had laid out a large red cross to indicate that, under the Geneva Convention, the adjacent area should be immune from attack.

The illusion that the red cross gave protection was rudely shattered when my morning shave was disturbed by nearby machine-gun fire and it was obvious that a fighter squadron was engaged in shooting up the area. Before this particular morning, the hope had been expressed that we might be sent casualties more quickly after their wounding, but none of us welcomed the alternative of seeing them occur on our own doorstep. At first it was assumed that the attack was by the Japanese, but then it was realised with horror that the planes were Hurricanes bearing RAF markings. At 0800 hours, after the squadron had departed in a northerly direction, there was a spell of intense activity to sort out the shambles.

The men of the Field Ambulance quickly transferred survivors to the adjacent *bashas* for first-aid measures and resuscitation. After preliminary assessment, No 7 was ready at 0900 hours to start the operating list, which continued throughout that day and night. From amongst the casualties, I shall always remember a tall Pathan, Shev Ram. During the round of inspection, it was seen that he had an open chest wound which had been covered by a field dressing. At first it seemed that Shev Ram would not survive long enough to reach the operating table; he lay motionless, hardly breathing and no pulse could be felt at the wrist.

The Pathan then opened his eyes and it was realised that he was fully alert and was conserving, as best he could, his ebbing strength. Another palpation of the wrist still failed to detect any pulse, but elsewhere pulses could be felt; the explanation was that here was an example of one of those rare anatomical variations in which the radial artery did not occupy its usual position over the bone at the wrist.

At this point it should be explained that in an open chest wound, the lung collapses on the side of the injury. When attempts are made to take deep breaths, air passes in and out of the chest opening without expanding the lung. Should the wounded man become agitated and start violently fighting for his breath, his respiratory efforts produce a side-to-side flapping movement in the compartment occupied by the heart and great vessels (mediastinum). This so-called mediastinal flap is liable to disturb the functioning of the heart that death rapidly ensues.

By lying perfectly still and reducing respiratory movement to a minimum, Shev Ram had managed to avoid this fatal complication. His chest and lung injuries were dealt with under local block anaesthesia and then it was seen that there was a hole in the right diaphragm, indicating that the bullet had passed on into the abdomen. The chest wound was then closed and after a break of twenty minutes for further resuscitation, the abdomen was opened under general anaesthesia to allow liver bleeding to be stopped and a lacerated duodenum repaired.

The Pathan proved to be a most co-operative patient who, without a word of complaint, submitted to drip, gastric suction and closed drainage of the chest; the post-operative course was uneventful and he made a complete recovery from his thoraco-abdominal injuries. In these present days of violence, any civilian may be called upon to give first-aid measures; when confronted with a blowing chest wound, the application of a bulky dressing to block the hole, could keep the victim alive until medical help could be given.

Within twenty-four hours of the shoot-up, we had a visit from a high-ranking RAF investigation team; they obtained eye-witness accounts of the attack and took away with them bullets which had been removed at operation. In due course it was confirmed that the RAF had been responsible and following a court of enquiry, this particular squadron was withdrawn for further training. After the incident, a red cross was never again displayed and we greeted any plane with a barrage from the ground, without awaiting identification as to whether it was Japanese or British. It should be stated that no hits were recorded. In this part of Arakan, the attitude towards the RAF remained hostile for many weeks.

At the time it was difficult to understand how such a tragic error could have happened, but a year later, after flying over the same area in a mail plane, I realised how easily pilots could lose their bearings. At Cox's Bazar, I had sought to hitch an air lift to Chittagong and found an Anson pilot who said he would oblige provided that first he could complete his trip south to drop mail. After we had become airborne, I noticed that the pilot was studying a map taken from a child's school atlas. He admitted that previously he had never flown over the area and he welcomed my offer of navigational assistance.

Although I had just spent a year in this part of Burma, even when flying low above the thick forest and numerous waterways, it was none too easy to guide the plane to Bawli Bazar. Here the first mail drop was made through the side door of the aircraft and then, after stimulating though ineffective ground fire when we accidentally strayed over the Japanese lines, we got back on course to repeat the exercise at Maungdaw. Thereafter there were no navigational problems as all that was required was to follow the coastline of the Teknaf peninsula in a northerly direction. During the last stage of the flight, at an altitude of several thousand feet, we were given a sudden thorough shaking when the pilot had to take quick evasive action to avoid collision with a high-flying vulture! I later learned that this particular Anson mail plane had been due for a major overhaul; before this could be carried out, it crashed on the next trip south and the pilot lost his life.

CHAPTER EIGHT

The Team

When at full strength, No 7 was a team of some eighteen men. A general surgical specialist acted as officer in command and during the life of the unit, this position was in turn held by Majors Saxton, Hooper, Baty, Dickinson and Wilson. I was fortunate to have as second-in-command Major George Quayle who, in addition to his work in anaesthetics and resuscitation, had a great contribution to make towards the smooth running of the unit. He was thoroughly reliable in his work and a most entertaining companion during relaxation, when we were very much in each other's pockets.

Towards the end of our year-long association, we both were becoming somewhat touchy and small items of disagreement became exaggerated out of all proportion. George complained that I was issuing orders without informing him; I, in turn, insisted that he had been told. At the time neither of us realised that George was developing a progressive nerve deafness. The third doctor, Subidhar Karem Singh, had qualified in India and was a King's Commissioned Officer; this Sikh, as well as assisting at operations, fluently spoke many dialects, a talent which made him an invaluable company officer.

A very important member of the team was Corporal Cross, who had the physique of Henry Cooper and the facial expressions of Tommy Cooper. He concerned himself with the running of the operating theatre, including sterilisation, care of equipment and maintenance of supplies. Thanks to Corporal Cross, No 7 always managed to improve on its equipment when it moved from one field ambulance to join another. Mainly engaged as theatre nurses were Anturash and Shrider, high caste Indians who helped with anaesthetics, drips and plastering and might be employed as additional assistants at operations. Nursing care was provided by three British orderlies, two unrelated Taylors and one Shufflebotham. In addition, eventually there arrived half a dozen nursing sepoys who required some instruction when it was discovered that they were recording temperatures and pulse rates without using either thermometer or watch.

The chief Indian driver, Appa Sab, was, to put it mildly, lacking in experience. He was liable to lose his ignition key at most inconvenient times such as when the military situation required us to make a speedy move. On one occasion he managed to run off the road with the main equipment truck; as the three-tonner lay on its side, he remained at the driver's seat producing a steady blast on the horn. On enquiring about this unseemly noise, his reply was:

'Regulations, Sahib; in case of accident, horn must be blown!'

At least Appa Sab checked petrol levels with a dip-stick and was not one of those unfortunates who, once only, favoured the use of a lighted match. In the course of twelve months, treatment was required for perhaps half a dozen Indian drivers with severe burns sustained as a result of using this method of checking petrol levels in their vehicles.

Dhobi Ram Dyal attended to all the laundry work of the unit and he was able to produce spotless clothes, gowns and sheets with the expenditure of much energy and very little soap. The grand old man was sweeper Nanoo, a so-called Untouchable who belonged to the lowest Hindu caste. He attended to the latrines and carried out general cleaning work which, for religious reasons, could not be undertaken by the higher caste sepoys. Once Nanoo unfortunately overstayed his leave by one month and on his return some disciplinary action was required. His pay was docked and he was officially given a fortnight's prison sentence; the latter was a token punishment since we had no prison and he was therefore detailed to sleep in the Field Ambulance's guardroom *basha* which was reasonably comfortable. As there was no one else to do his work, each day he was freed to get on with his duties as a sweeper. Being a powerful server of the volley-ball and one of the main stays of the unit's team, he was brought out of confinement to play in matches. It was some months later, when No 7 was cut off by the Japanese, that he and I shared a slit-trench for the night.

From amongst the nursing sepoys, it was not difficult to find batmen whose minimal extra duties supplemented their pay. I was landed with a Bengali named Banzi who, with his rolling eyes and perpetual grin, looked like a straight-haired golliwog. This character nearly always managed to do what he considered to be for the best, irrespective of what careful instructions had been given to him. When sent to nearby Bawli Bazar to buy matches, invariably he brought no change, having used the balance to purchase bundles of stinking cheroots and highly-coloured sweetmeats he thought I might like; in due course he enjoyed them himself. His idea of making tea was to warm up milk, sugar and tea together to produce an insipid mixture with leaves floating on top. On the rare occasions when I could hope for the treat of a lightly boiled egg, he would present the bantam eggs rock hard after twenty minutes of boiling, in spite of careful instructions not to boil for more than two minutes.

Once, during a quiet period, Banzi accompanied me on a short visit back to Calcutta where I attended a surgical conference. We had to stay for the night each way as we passed through Tumbru. After dark, when Banzi and I came to the entrance of No 46 Field Ambulance, suddenly a couple of Indian guards brought us to a halt with fixed bayonets against our chests and the demand for the password. Fortunately the word '*Chini*' eased the situation and Banzi was able to stop rolling his eyes. In marked contrast to the steadily improving morale in forward areas, it was most noticeable that, on the lines of communication, many personnel were in a jittery, trigger-happy state; we were fortunate to escape being shot during the delay before I remembered the password and stopped Banzi from making a dash for it into the jungle.

We both agreed quite soon that Tumbru had about it a sickly, all-pervading smell which had not been present when No 7 had worked there a few months previously. On mentioning this to Colonel Healey, he told me that a fortnight previously they had first been aware of the smell and since no source for it had been discovered, it was concluded that rats were responsible and to the residents it had gradually become hardly noticeable. When we next passed through Tumbru a week later, the obnoxious odour was no longer in evidence; it seemed that our earlier visit had stimulated another intense search which had revealed a small, overgrown *basha* occupied by a decaying corpse. The body had become luminous and men had to don their gas-masks to face the stench of the *basha* and remove the remains for burial. This was one of the few occasions that gas-masks served a useful purpose. Fortunately, neither the Allies nor the Japanese ever added gas to the tribulations of jungle warfare but even so, No 7, from time to time, carried out respirator drills, in due course becoming proficient in the speedy donning of gas-masks.

In the latter part of 1943, when Banzi and I went through Chittagong, Bengal was experiencing a severe famine which created more devastation than the war itself. In the station, the Indian Railway men and porters carried out their ordinary duties, ignoring the many pathetic bundles of dirty clothing covering the bodies of the dead and dying scattered along the platform. Banzi himself, with true Eastern resignation, showed little concern for the harrowing sights; his main interest was that I should place an order for a special deck chair to be made by one of his numerous relatives. It was most clearly impressed upon him that no deck chair was to be ordered on my behalf, but on our way back through Chittagong he appeared with the chair and the bill. On this occasion he did not get his way; I refused to buy the chair and he was lumbered with it. He humped it on and off the Cox's Bazar steamer and then back to Bawli, no doubt expecting me to change my mind.

During the succeeding months, whenever the opportunity occurred, Banzi could be seen enjoying relaxation in his chair as he puffed away at a stinking cheroot. On one occasion he was put on a rota for maintaining artificial respiration on a man with a self-inflicted wound in the head. The patient's heart continued to beat but respiration had failed; circulation would cease as soon as artificial respiration was discontinued. Because of extensive brain damage the case was quite hopeless, but all members of the unit were in turn used, in order to give them training. When Banzi was put on the job, it was considered desirable to check on his activities after a few minutes; as I expected, he had taken a rest to enjoy a smoke, but as soon as he caught sight of me the cigarette was doused and he quickly re-applied his hands to the chest, once again to restore a feeble pulse. After several hours and the need to deal with other casualties, artificial respiration was discontinued.

Banzi had the distinction of being the only member of the unit to sustain a wound as the indirect result of enemy action. He was a passenger in a truck travelling along a road subjected to periodic mortar fire; although ordered to stay put, a near miss was too much for him and he decided to take off from the truck as it was making all possible speed along this section of the road. The dash had to be temporarily halted to allow for Banzi to be bundled back; his trousers had been torn to ribbons and he had sustained a cut thigh which required a couple of stitches.

For extra nursing aid, for supplies and for feeding, the Mobile Unit relied upon its attachment to either a CCS or the MDS of a Field Ambulance. From the feeding aspect, we favoured messing with the Indian units whose cooks were able to work wonders with bully beef fried with onions or combined with curry and rice. In our experience the British cooks could not rise above anything more inspiring than bully beef sliced or in a stew with dehydrated potatoes; sometimes there was a change to soya bean sausages. The sweet was usually tinned fruit, but in season we enjoyed ripe mangoes; more frequently, the fresh fruit was the jungle banana with its numerous hard pips.

Quartermaster Kifford of the Field Ambulance was able, keen and obliging; it was unfortunate for him that, in the space of a few weeks, he sustained three disappointments. Anxious to see his first major operation, he attended the theatre and during conversation let slip that his blood group was O/4. Blood was urgently needed for the particular operation and Kifford supplied the necessary couple of pints of this much-in-demand blood group. Instead of watching the operation, he spent the time at rest on an adjacent bed. A few days later, he managed to shoot one of the long-legged white birds which haunted the paddy fields and nearby *chaungs* to pick up a living from small fry. At the evening meal, the paddy bird, which was the size of a small chicken, occupied the whole of his plate; the golden brown carcase was a mouth-watering sight, especially for those of us served with bully beef. Kifford's much publicised feast started with a ceremonious sweep of the knife through the tough skin, whereupon the bird collapsed like a pricked balloon. After much picking and searching, the only end result was a single mouthful of tough tasteless meat. All but Kifford joined in the roars of laughter which echoed through the surrounding jungle.

His third disappointment was rather sad, in more ways than one. A small Burmese boy, aged about seven, had lost both his parents and during his transit through the Field Ambulance had attached himself to Kifford. The quartermaster had arranged for his 'adopted' son to be fitted with khaki shorts and a toy wooden sword. Kim, which was the name given to the boy by Kifford, often paraded and drilled as he played at soldiers; like a pet dog, he followed the QM everywhere. Unfortunately the crunch soon came when it was discovered that rum was missing from the stores. The culprit was Kim who, in a very short time, had developed a flourishing black market with the natives of nearby Bawli. He had to be promptly evacuated to the orphanage at Chittagong, so bringing to an end an impossible situation.

Whilst we were associated with the No 66 Field Ambulance, the adjacent river Pruma was the source of several unusual cases. A native in his *sampan* was hit by a cannon shell fired from an aircraft and the missile entered through the right lower chest to pass completely through the body. The patient remained alive for an hour after reaching the unit where it was found that the man's liver had been completely destroyed, nothing remaining but a sac of bloody pulp; it was amazing that such a terrible explosive injury had not produced instant death.

One morning, the river yielded up a corpse which must have been immersed for several weeks. The scavengers, probably crabs, had removed all the soft tissues from the head to leave a bare skull which was attached to a brownish-black, distended body covered with remnants of unidentifiable clothing. There was no bullet wound or evidence of injury and it was quite impossible even to guess the cause of death. Nothing remained to give a clue to the identity of the individual and even his race was a matter of doubt. He was certainly not Indian since, under the remains of the collar-band, there was a circle of white skin; it could not be settled whether he was British or Japanese. The uncovered corpse had been laid on a stretcher in the reception *basha*.

At this time, some minor operation had been carried out on a BOR (British Other Rank), the anaesthetic being pentothal. As the soldier was coming round, he was taken from the theatre by a couple of orderlies who laid the stretcher down next to the corpse. When the patient fully regained consciousness, he turned his head and on opening his eyes was confronted with the sight of the bared skull! His screams brought us rushing from the theatre to calm him down and get the situation under control. The man's nervous system withstood this needless shock and later he explained that, as he came round, the horrible sight that greeted him made him believe that he had died and landed in Hell.

In contrast, a river coolie demonstrated that the after-effects of pentothal could be enjoyable. He had presented himself with bad toothache from a carious molar which I extracted; when the effect of the intra-venous anaesthetic wore off, he began laughing and singing, thoroughly revelling in his state of intoxication. A week later he was back again to have another bad tooth taken out, to be followed by a similar performance. After a few more days, he once again appeared, this time pointing to a perfectly healthy tooth which he wished to have removed. Before he was sent on his way without further dentistry, an interpreter questioned him. The man admitted that, in order to enjoy the after effects of pentothal, he was prepared to part with all his teeth one at a time.

At irregular intervals we had visitations and inspections from high-ranking combatant officers. One such visitor enquired as to the number of operations which could be carried out in, say, twelve hours; when it was pointed out to him that the number depended upon the type of operation necessary, he quickly remarked:

'That was a bloody silly question, was it not?'

He took no exception to my reply.

'It certainly was.'

Some visitors held the view that the greater priority should be given to the less severely wounded as these men could be quickly salvaged to fight again. Fortunately for general morale, the need to make such a choice never arose for No 7. Whilst the very ill patients were being resuscitated, we and the Field Ambulance attended to minor cases. The badly wounded men were taken into the theatre as and when they had been brought into a fit state to stand anaesthetic and operation. Between major operations, minor injuries were fitted into the list or, without any harm, delayed until the more seriously injured had been operated on. Apart from times of battle and disaster, the conditions pertaining in Burma usually prevented the delivery of large numbers of casualties all at once. For several hours, a wounded man might be carried through the jungle by a friend before finding a bearer unit which, in turn, invariably had a difficult journey before reaching an ADS (Advanced Dressing Station) for first aid measures. The next stage from ADS to MDS (Main Dressing Station) could mean further delay, caused by bad road conditions so that the surgical unit usually had time to cope with one load of wounded before another ambulance got through.

Towards the end of November 1943, we were sorry that No 66 Field Ambulance had to move on and be replaced by No 15 CCS which at this time, for political reasons, was commanded by a Sikh. One of his first acts was to send for me and demand a list of personnel of No 7 so that he could allocate them to duties in his CCS. In no uncertain terms, I pointed out to him that he was overstepping his authority; when necessary No 7 worked all out for many hours without a break, but when there were no casualties requiring attention, the unit would rest and re-organise its equipment. Reluctantly, he had to accept this statement but, in retaliation, frequently had his orderly deliver to me chits requesting my attendance in his office to discuss some trivial matter.

On one such occasion, I was standing in front of his desk, listening to some involved complaint about one of my unit, when we heard the drone of a squadron of Japanese bombers passing high overhead, bound for the north. The discourse came to an abrupt end when, without another word, the Colonel and his Indian office staff stampeded out of the *basha* to disappear into adjacent slit trenches until the squadron was well out of sight and sound.

I was still waiting at his desk when he returned, but the incident seemed to have shaken him to such an extent that I was dismissed from his presence without any further discussion of the subject. As a counter measure to the numerous pin-pricks and in order to bring some light relief, arrangements were made for the colonel to receive a stream of reports delivered at all hours of the day and night. On the top of each note was placed a reference number after the letters 'BTU'; it would not be difficult for any soldier to guess for what the letters stood. In addition, to each note was added the words 'Copy to ADMS', but these copies were never forwarded. The colonel finally asked for a truce in correspondence when note BTU 32 was delivered to him whilst he was having his evening bath.

After several weeks, it was felt that it would be desirable to visit Brigadier Meneces to explain that the O/C of No 7 MSU and the present O/C of No 15 CCS were incompatible. Within a short time, we received the welcome order to move forward south of the river, to join the Main Dressing Station of No 10 Field Ambulance.

CHAPTER NINE

Thank God for Bamboo

The equipment of the unit was limited and much of it was poor in quality. It was soon discovered that artery forceps stamped with the mark 'Imperial' were liable to spring open or break in half during use. These defective forceps were put on one side and, even when not in use, they broke spontaneously, the metal failing to accommodate to the temperature variations between day and night. It seems possible that the suggestion that these forceps were bazaar-made by small boys, using old petrol tins, might well be true. When the situation in Arakan became more fluid, higher authority impressed upon us the importance of burying instruments at night to prevent them falling into enemy hands, unless of course, we were using them ourselves.

In my reply I pointed out that it would assist the Allied Cause if 'Imperial' forceps were captured by the Japanese, in fact these instruments could prove to be a secret weapon. To one visiting brigadier, I suggested that the O/C of No 7 might be sent back to the UK to make rounds of the voluntary hospitals and seek donations of forceps. He thought that the idea was worth considering but if such a suggestion was approved, he would be the one to volunteer for this duty. Unfortunately, neither of us was given authorisation to undertake the proposed trip.

For intestinal work in civilian surgery, it is usual to employ special needles into the ends of which are blended lengths of catgut. These atraumatic needles have no bulge at the junction between needle and catgut so that a smooth passage through the bowel wall is facilitated. In Arakan, when the original supply of atraumatic needles was exhausted, it came as something of a shock to find in the replacement packets (made in India), the catgut lengths, not attached to the needles themselves having no eyes. Fortunately in my well-stocked 'hussif' were many reels of thread together with a good supply of household needles; thereafter, these were used for all intestinal work without any resulting complications.

Quite often, when dealing with abdominal wounds, a section of damaged bowel might require removal and continuity would have to be re-established by making a leakproof junction (anastomosis) between healthy bowel ends. During this part of the operation, in order to avoid leakage of bowel contents, it is usual to make use of special clamps which lightly grip the bowel without causing any damage. Our 'Imperial' occlusion clamps soon snapped without warning and so a technique was developed to carry out anastomosis without using clamps; the method proved so satisfactory that it was retained after return to civilian life.

Word had filtered back to India about our deficiencies and when the Consultant Surgeon, Colonel Gardham, visited us, he handed over an ancient but well-equipped case of British surgical instruments. He would be unlikely ever to forget his visit, for it nearly cost him his life. He sailed to us in *Elsa*, which had continued upstream to Bawli bridge and the intention was that he should be picked up on her return journey to Tumbru Ghat. His visit was cut short when a message was received that the steamer would need to move on as the anchors were failing to hold her against the swollen torrent of the Pruma. We saw the Colonel down to the jetty where he boarded a small *sampan* which shot out towards *Elsa* as she rolled in mid-stream. A rope was thrown to the craft and, as soon as it was grasped, the strength of the current forced down the prow of the *sampan* which immediately began to ship water in large quantities. The holding-rope had to be paid out to avoid further swamping and *Elsa* had to move gradually down stream until both craft could be brought side to side; then, whilst steamer and *sampan* swept along at the same speed, a soaked but otherwise safe Colonel Gardham was hauled aboard.

Soon afterwards, a civilian was admitted on account of a head injury which he had sustained by falling off Bawli bridge. When first seen, he was semi-conscious and was lying beside the bed using a bed-pan as a pillow. In addition to the presence of bruising over one temple, it was noted that a pupil was widely dilated and this, combined with other features, led to a diagnosis of intra-cranial haemorrhage from a meningeal artery. The damaged artery, which lies in a grove on the inner side of the thin temporal bone, was steadily producing a collection of blood clot between the skull and the membrane covering the brain. In order to relieve the increasing pressure on the brain and to stop the bleeding, the skull had to be opened. Fortunately in Colonel Gardham's surgical case, there was a good trephine (instrument for removing a disc of skull bone) and special wire saws which did not snap. After we had taken away part of the skull and turned out the blood clot, the compressed brain expanded; bleeding was controlled and in due course, the patient made a complete recovery.

Within twenty-four hours another severe injury was admitted; he was a high-ranking Japanese officer with a bullet in his head. At this time we had the additional benefit of radiology from a unit attached to the CCS; the films showed that the bullet had lodged in the left side of the brain in the region of the large lateral venous channel. Eventually the bullet was extracted but several hours later the patient died without regaining consciousness. Apart from the radiology at Bawli, this facility was not elsewhere available but, by and large, we managed quite well without it.

The unit eventually became truly mobile early in January 1944, when, for the first time, we were able to move forward in our own transport which consisted of one 3-tonner, two 15 cwt trucks and two station wagons. It was not long before we became proficient in the speedy packing and unpacking of panniers; we soon learnt how to put up tents to the best advantage. Two EPIP (English Pattern-Indian Pattern) tents linked together provided space for resuscitation and operating; a smaller tent, opening off the main theatre, accommodated steriliser and autoclave. It was an advantage to select a site beside a hill which, in addition to giving protection, could be dug out to increase working room. One side of the tent roofing would be slung up above the dug-out area to provide greater headroom and at the same time a useful shelf could be cut from the earth. When time permitted, after putting up the main poles, the floor was lowered by further excavation and the operating table was positioned on the rubber matting which Major Hooper had salvaged from Maungdaw. The remainder of the theatre floor was solid earth the surface of which was swept and then treated with old engine-oil; soon, the resulting surface became firm, dust free and capable of being washed down. During the daytime, it was possible to get more air by having one side of the theatre tent rolled up and replaced by green-stained mosquito netting. No red crosses were shown and by draping over the foliage of palm, bamboo and banana leaves the outlines of the tentage were made to blend with the surrounding jungle. We had, of course, to check the camouflage regularly to make sure that any wilting greenery was replaced. After sundown, the theatre needed to be both insect and light proof; the inner lining of mosquito netting restricted the entry of most insects and their further control came from the use of a Lysol spray between operations.

For some weeks, experiments were made to find a decent sucker which would prove effective in clearing blood from an operation wound. Eventually a most satisfactory piece of apparatus was evolved; a sterilised short glass tube was connected to rigid rubber tubing which passed up to a large air-tight bottle fixed to the tent pole; from the bottle further tubing went through the tent roof down to the station wagon which had been driven in close. The screen-wiper attachment on the induction pipe was disconnected and replaced by the tubing issuing from the theatre. With the engine ticking over, strong negative pressure was created in the bottle to produce admirable suction at the operation site. In order to avoid delivering blood into the engine, an obvious precaution to take was to discontinue suction before the bottle filled to the top.

Burma is a land wreathed in bamboos and the whole existence of the Burmese is bound with them. They play a very important role in his world, providing his house, his furniture, utensils, farm implements, baskets, containers, binding materials and some of his food; in fact, the rural Burman cannot imagine an existence in a country without bamboos, and we visitors soon felt the impact upon our lives. After jungle patrols, it was not uncommon to receive a soldier who had accidentally sustained a soft tissue wound from bamboo splinters and on occasion, casualties came from booby traps laced with hidden bamboo spikes.

The injuries sustained from bamboo were more than compensated for by the numerous benefits it bestowed. Medical officers were soon, as a routine, employing strips of bamboo for first-aid splintage and the surgical unit made full use of this all-providing plant to supplement deficiencies in equipment. Rigid tubes of any length or calibre were readily available and were used for the suspension of lights over the operating table. Across the threatre, from the junctions of side wall and roof, were fixed two slender bamboo poles; on these, two short, wider sections were threaded and bound together with thick wire to hold two Jeep headlamps. A 6-volt battery supplied the lighting which could be slid backwards or forwards over the full length of the table and lateral tilt could be achieved by a little manipulation of the long tubes. This contraption was an adaption of the method employed by the Burmese, who used sliding flaps carried on bamboo tubes to cover the window openings in their bashas.

For injuries involving the shoulder and upper arm, some special form of immobilisation was required after operation. To hold the damaged arm in the correct position, the so-called thoraco-brachial plaster was applied; this plaster encircled the chest whilst the injured arm, also in plaster, was fixed away from the trunk at near a right angle. When applying a thoraco-brachial plaster to an unconscious patient, the top of the operating table was dropped and the patient's head was supported by a petrol tin placed on the top of a couple of panniers; the main weight of the trunk was taken by a strip of bamboo which had been covered by a well-vaselined bandage. From air-tight tins, numbered lengths of plaster of Paris were soaked and the slabs applied in rota. At the time when it was the policy to have the arm abducted, rigid support for this was obtained by incorporating within the plaster a short half section of bamboo which acted as a bridge between the lower chest and the abducted arm. When the plaster had set, the vaselined support was slipped out from the back. The theatre staff, in particular Antrage and Shredar, became most proficient in the application of this type of plaster and their record time for the procedure was seven minutes.

Basin supports were made from thick 3-foot lengths of bamboo which were driven through the earthen floor of the theatre; after a series of splits had been made into the upper end of the tube, plaster of Paris was used to fix this piece of theatre furniture into a splayed circular shape to hold a basin. With a little modification it was possible to convert a basin support into a serviceable peg-leg; once a one-legged native drifted in from the jungle to amble away again in a few hours highly delighted with his new limb. It is impossible to do more then mention the splints, spreaders, walking plasters and all manner of appliances made from the all-purpose material available on the spot.

Absent from the unit's equipment was the proctoscope, an instrument used for inspecting the anal canal and rectum; through this instrument, possible rectal injuries can be diagnosed or haemorrhoids injected. We were able to construct a most serviceable substitute using cork, wire and of course, bamboo. It was frequently in use until replaced by a proper metal instrument; Brigadier Naunton Morgan took the original and said he would be presenting it to the Imperial War Museum. From the experience gained in Burma, I was able to write a memorandum entitled 'The surgical uses of bamboo'; it might have helped others working in similar conditions but I did not feel that it was worth while submitting it for publication in the UK where surgeons managed reasonably well without bamboo.

The most satisfactory set-up was when No 7 had the support of a transfusion unit which not only contributed a great deal in effecting a rapid turn over of cases but also salvaged many who otherwise might have been lost. Captain Paddy Renaine was in charge of such a unit making himself responsible for both pre- and post-operative resuscitation. A badly wounded man might be brought in by bearer units and on admission appear to be in a hopeless state; after perhaps an hour of concentrated effort, during which many pints of blood had been transfused under pressure, a head would appear round the theatre entrance and Paddy would announce that the patient was fit for anaesthetic and operation.

Usually we were able to get adequate supplies of sterile fluid for intravenous use and we never had to resort to coconut milk as a substitute. On rare occasions when the stock of sterile fluid was getting low, Corporal Cross, using one of the primus stoves, got busy with distillation. These stoves normally were employed for autoclaving and for the sterilisation of instruments; this activity was restricted to a small tent opening on to the main theatre. One night there was quite a 'flap' when the tent roof caught fire; thereafter we took special precautions which included soaking the tent roof with water before a sterilisation session and restricting these activities to daylight hours.

At this stage of the war, antibiotics had not reached the East and reliance had to be placed upon sulphonamides which were introduced locally, by mouth and intravenously. A year later, when I was in charge of the 14th Army Penicillin Research Unit, nearly 50% of infecting bacteria were found to be insensitive to penicillin. In Arakan, limb wounds were laid open to relieve tension; damaged muscle and bone fragments were removed and no attempt was made to stitch the wound. The saucerised area created was sprayed with sulphathiazole powder and a protection of vaselined lint was laid on the raw surface before applying the appropriate split plaster or splintage. With an indelible pencil, the plasters were marked with the date of the operation and a rough diagram was made to indicate the extent of the bone damage. If abdominal wounds were completely closed, even with drains in position, they invariably developed gross infection, so it became the policy to leave open both skin and fat. After perhaps ten days, a clean wound would be ready for delayed suturing. Until they learnt better, some newcomers to jungle surgery tended to make a too-limited exposure of the deeper tissues and then plug the wound tightly with lengths of vaseline gauze; this method invariably led to complications.

Extensive skin loss could be a problem and at a much later date, Major Eric Peet and I had discussions on this subject at his plastic surgery unit in Secunderabad, Deccan. An idea developed that he should, from volunteers, take split skin grafts which could be frozen and distributed to the small refrigerators carried by transfusion units. Although from another person, such a graft could be expected to survive for perhaps up to a fortnight before being rejected and during this time it would give a protective skin covering until the patient reached base hospital. This research was not followed up because the war against Japan was brought to a speedy conclusion by the atomic bomb.

The post-operative ward was made from a series of linked tents, next to the theatre and hidden in the bushes. After abdominal operations, gastric suction was desirable until the patient was able to pass flatus. Since we had not been issued with the special gastric suction tubes, ordinary rigid rubber tubing had to be used. It was not easy for a patient to swallow such tubing and whenever possible it was introduced whilst he was still under the anaesthetic.

At times it was difficult to make a patient understand the need for uncomfortable measures.

I well remember a Gurkha with an abdominal wound for which after operation, drip and suction were set up; when he came round from the anaesthetic, he repeatedly pulled out both the intravenous drip and the gastric suction. After many re-insertions, eventually, through an interpreter, the patient passed on the message that he had lost all faith in me and he would not tolerate such treatment which, he insisted, his own village doctor would never have thought of using on him. There was no alternative but to let him have his own way and he proved his point by making a good recovery.

The Gurkhas were certainly memorable characters. When having their wounds dressed they usually submitted without complaint other than the emission of a series of 'Ay, Ay, Ayes'. If, after operation, they woke to find that the plasters were, in their opinion, unduly restricting their activities, they did not hesitate to work all night cutting off offending plaster. Next day, they submitted to re-plastering with a grin and the usual 'Ay, Ayes'. As fighting men, the Gurkhas were without equal. Their razor-sharp *kukris* struck terror into the Japanese who could be decapitated in a flash. It is said that in their native Nepal, before youths could be regarded as having reached manhood, an initiation ceremony would be held; at it, with a single sweep of his kukri, the young Gurkha was required to sever completely the head of a bullock. No doubt if he failed in this, he would be required to take the test again after further practice. Quite apart from their skill in jungle warfare, the Gurkhas were often selected as reliable guards for Japanese prisoners. One morning, a surgeon visiting the post-operative ward, found that his Japanese patient had had his throat cut; the guard explained that this had been necessary as he caught the prisoner trying to escape. From the surgical point of view, the would-be escaper could not have got very far with a gun-shot wound of femur immobilised in Thomas splint and plaster!

When the situation permitted, it was desirable to retain post-operative abdominal cases for at least a week before arranging evacuation. If patients with abdominal wounds had to be moved on immediately or soon after operation, some failed to survive the journey. Although from the surgical point of view the chance of survival was increased by holding patients to continue with drip and suction until bowel tone had recovered, this was not always possible because of the over-ruling military situation. Although beneficial for their surgical condition, those post-operative abdominal patients who were retained often had little peace. During the day-time, there was the added discomfort from heat, thirst and flies; at night sleep was difficult because of nearby gunfire and the ever-present threat of a visit from a Japanese patrol.

On looking over No 7's theatre book in which were recorded details of injury, the anaesthetic, the operation and the progress, it was of interest to note that some casualties from most units serving in the Arakan had their names in that book. In addition to those from the British county regiments and various Indian Rifle brigades, it was surprising the number of wounded that came to us from mule companies, bearer units, field ambulances and the civil population. Men of the 'V' Force, that little known para-military unit which gathered information from behind the enemy lines, if wounded, usually fell into Jap hands and were shot. A member of the Force was Suleman whose right shoulder had been shattered by a bullet. With an improvised dressing covering his wounds, he had avoided Japanese patrols and without food or drink for 24 hours had scrambled through thick jungle to reach us at Bawli Bazar in surprisingly good condition for the necessary operation.

Quite apart from the large number of war wounds involving head, neck, trunk and limbs, acute cases unconnected with the Japanese or the jungle not infrequently presented themselves. Several mastoid operations were required, many carious teeth had to be removed, abscesses needed drainage and even circumcisions were necessary. During my time with the unit, I never encountered an acute appendix and I was never called upon to turn my hand to any gynaecology or obstetrics!

CHAPTER TEN

Full House

Throughout the year, between violent periods of activity in the field there were many hours of potential boredom broken only by the receipt of mail from home. An airmail letter card from the UK usually took a fortnight, but not infrequently, because of unit movements, delay was much longer. It was often necessary to search round for a Field Post Office in the hopes that, when found, there might be the reward of a large bundle of letters. In addition to the writing of letters to one's family, it became the practice to correspond with the Higher Authorities in New Delhi. In no uncertain terms the unit's deficiencies were pointed out by us; both George Quayle and I sent in reports suggesting improvements in the set-up and use of mobile units. We stressed the benefits that would come from the supply of a specially fitted vehicle into which would be fixed the autoclave and a chore-horse for charging batteries. For speedy packing we proposed that theatre equipment should be so designed that it could be readily fitted into less cumbersome panniers. With diagrams we explained how a cage of mosquito netting could be used in conjunction with a different tentage. Finally we went to town on instrument quality and deficiencies. It seemed that all our criticism and advice fell on deaf ears, but somewhat belatedly, in fact about five years after the war, the War Office sent me war equipment tables (WET) which were being revised for mobile surgical units. I was asked to give my comments and suggestions!

The O/C of every unit was required each month to submit personnel strength returns. At one stage, I stopped sending these returns and this action produced from India, a frantic flurry of 'top secret', 'urgent' and 'confidential messages'. In reply I pointed out that, from the previous returns, they would have seen that No 7, the only surgical unit then working in the Arakan, was under-strength in both British and Indian orderlies. It was made quite clear that until they paid some attention to the returns and made good the deficiencies, New Delhi need not expect further reports from me. Within a fortnight the unit was brought up to full strength! Thereafter Higher Authority had the returns regularly and the matter ended. When our monthly pay chits arrived, we were somewhat annoyed to note that there had been deductions for heat, lighting and running water. We pointed out that we were not living in an Indian garrison town, our heat came from the sun, the light was from a hurricane lamp and the only running water was from the monsoon. On this subject, we composed stinging letters to the Pay Department, but from our point of view, no progress was made. In Arakan we were in the happy position of being able to tell the pundits back in India what we thought of them, knowing full well that they could not post us anywhere as a punishment; any posting in the entire theatre of war could only have been for the better.

Old newspapers from home were eagerly seized upon and any form of novel was considered a prize. At night, before settling down, it might be possible to read by the light of a hurricane lamp, for at least an hour. Even when we moved into areas where there was a strict blackout, a reading session could be achieved under a blanket using an electric torch.

At Tumbru, where I shared a *basha* with George Quayle, we had long sessions at cards. Two-handed patience was played until we got to hate the sound of the word 'Huff'. Then, for a time, bezique became popular and was continued until we both had had our fill of the sight of the Queen of Spades and the Jack of Diamonds.

It was at Tumbru that I was initiated into the volley-ball game in which nine men on each side of a high net, using their hands, drove a large ball back and forth in the air, three touches being permitted on each side. At the net, George Quayle, because of his height and skill, was ideal for bringing off the winning smashes. Our best server was sweeper Nanoo, a keen player who never wanted to be on the losing side. If any member of the side made a duff stroke, Nanoo, who spoke neither English nor Hindi, had plenty to say. We realised that, in his own tongue, he was cursing us for any slip, but he could hardly be charged with insubordination.

At Bawli, No 7 volley ball team gained in skill and experience to such an extent that any challenger could be beaten. When there was no work, it never became necessary before sundown to order a volley-ball parade. Except during the monsoon, the unit would automatically make their way to the pitch marked out on a dry paddy field beside the Pruma. Later in the campaign, when we were cut off by the Japanese, it was considered desirable first to restrict and later stop volley-ball activities. As other units were moving into position to man the perimeter defences, it was rather out of place to have our team continually tripping out stripped for volley-ball.

In the mess, after the evening meal, the odd drink was enjoyed. The monthly ration per officer was one bottle of whisky, one bottle of rum, one bottle of gin and half a dozen beers. For those of us who preferred beer, it was not difficult to effect an exchange. In Arakan, a favoured cocktail was called *Zakmi Dil* which means 'wounded heart'; the name was taken from a once popular Pathan marching song. The cocktail was made up from equal parts of rum, gin and lime to produce a pleasant but potent mixture; if over-proof rum was employed, there was a marked increase in both the potency and temperature of the drink. On one occasion, Brigadier Winter produced a bottle of 'genuine Scotch Whisky', brewed in Calcutta; it was labelled 'Panther's Piss' which no doubt accurately described the taste!

In the evenings, self-entertainment revealed many hidden talents. There was the half-French lieutenant-colonel whose excellent conjuring shows continued until we found out how the illusions were created. Sometimes discussions were serious, but more often ridiculous arguments went on for ages. For example, much scientific thought was brought to bear on the subject of the relative potency of iced gin as compared with gin from a fridge; no facilities existed to settle this argument. Russian Roulette once became a subject for discussion; some insisted that, with a well-oiled revolver, the weight of the bullet would invariably bring the chamber to the safety of the 6 o'clock position. We did have the facilities for settling this argument but no one was disposed to put their theory to the test.

There was always someone to revive long forgotten jokes and bawdy recitations; one member of the mess could, with feeling and without forgetting a single word, recite the saga of 'Eskimo Nell' and when new members joined our gathering, he would be called upon to deliver his party piece. Entertaining stories were always involved and prolonged. It was at Bawli that I first listened to a medical tale which, years later, appeared in *Reader's Digest* in a somewhat modified version. It was claimed that there was an element of truth in the story which originated in Edinburgh.

The account concerns a young married couple with a bouncing baby of four months; they decided that it was high time that they had an evening out together. After a lot of hesitation and some difficulty, a suitable young woman was found to act as babysitter. Following their meal at the North British Hotel, they rang up their home to check that all was well; having got the necessary reassurance, they went to the Empire Theatre. At the interval, the wife again became anxious and another phone call was made but this time the husband failed to get any answer. The couple, much alarmed, quickly took a taxi back to their home to find the baby peacefully asleep in the nursery. At first there was no sign of the baby sitter but her calls directed them to the lavatory where they found her firmly attached to the seat. Before they had left, the husband had failed to tell her that that afternoon, he had freshly varnished the seat.

Initial attempts to pull her off only succeeded in producing cries of pain, so they sent for the local medical practitioner. He also failed, but in his effort he slipped and broke his ankle. The ambulance was then called and the attendants unscrewed the lavatory seat. The patient with the adherent seat and the doctor with the Pott's fracture, were conveyed in the same ambulance to the Royal Infirmary. The surgical chief was informed about this unusual admission and on his round next morning, decided to show it to some visiting American surgeons. After screens had been placed round the bed, he turned up the bed clothes to reveal the nether quarters of this unfortunate young woman. The visiting Americans showed suitable surprise and were at a loss what to say until one of their number came out with:

'Waal doc., I've seen many in my day but this is the first goddam one I've seen framed.'

Another story remains in the memory since it was first related by George Quayle, repeated by Bill Weston and later confirmed by Brigadier Nicholls (all St George's men). 'Nick' denied that he was the surgeon involved but gave the assurance that in every other respect the story was quite true.

It happened many years before the war, when a wealthy West-end family required surgical attention for their aged father. They were unwilling for the old gentleman to go into either hospital or nursing home to have his prostate removed. The famous surgeon agreed to carry out the operation provided adequate facilities could be arranged in the palatial residence. It was decided to convert the attic into a fully equipped operating theatre. The room was thoroughly cleaned; the roof and walls were then painted white for the special event. In due course, on the appointed evening, the surgeon arrived with his anaesthetist and theatre nurse. As the nurse made the final preparations, the surgeon chatted with the relatives in the drawing room. The first snag arose when a grandson of the patient stated that he was a medical student and demanded to be present at the operation. After much talk, the surgeon finally managed to dissuade the young man from attending.

Having reached the theatre in the newly installed lift, the anaesthetist who had intended to give a spinal anaesthetic, failed to get the lumbar puncture needle through the arthritic spine into the correct position and he had to abandon this procedure. As an alternative he turned to general anaesthesia and unfortunately, under chloroform induction, the creaking patient had a cardiac arrest which did not respond to cardiac massage. Surgeon and anaesthetist had to descend in the lift to break the tragic news to the relatives who, on the whole, were not surprised. The medical student however proved difficult and stated that, if he had been allowed to be present, he would never have agreed to the administration of chloroform to his grandfather. The surgeon who was a smooth talker, eventually settled them all; in fact they were at the stage of thanking him, when a loud scream reached their ears.

The whole company, ignoring the lift, rushed up the stairs and flinging open the door of the operating theatre were greeted by the sight of a blazing corpse. The scream had come from the nurse who had knocked over a bottle of surgical spirit which had become ignited from the electric fire. In spite of all their efforts, the flames quickly spread to the newly painted roof and the fire brigade had to be summoned. As the surgeon and anaesthetist left by the front door, the fire engine drew up and hoses were quickly brought into action. The surgeon turned to his colleague and remarked:

'George, I'm afraid we've left our mark on this house.'

Major Willie Wilson, who later took over as O/C of No 7, was at Bawli the surgeon of the nearby CCS. We had frequent visits from him and of an evening we were initiated into the technique of liar dice, a game which combined chance with skill and psychology. The learning process, at the stake of one rupee for three matches (lives), initially was quite expensive but in due course it became possible for me to pay my mess bills from my winnings. At the earlier sessions, the dice were shaken in a cup made from bamboo but this had to be replaced by a leather cup when the guards on Bawli bridge, a quarter of a mile away, reported that at night, they could clearly hear us rattling the dice.

On one occasion, during a late dice game, word was received that a Japanese patrol was in the immediate vicinity. The hurricane lamp was quickly doused and several officers seized their weapons before dashing out of the mess basha to join the search. No shots were heard and when the flap had settled the game was resumed after prolonged argument as to the exact state of play at the time of the interruption. Once a member of the dice school nearly got expelled when he surreptitiously replaced the dice by a very large beetle (popularly known as a flying fortress); it certainly produced a marked reaction when his opponent lifted the cup. It was surprising how many high-ranking officers and even a bishop, played the game of liar dice. One evening, a visiting general watched our play for a time and then with an innocent expression, enquired about the name and rules of the game. He asked if he might be permitted to join in and we agreed, looking forward to being able to relieve him of his spare rupees. After he had swept the board clean, we realised that this was not beginner's luck.

When Willie Wilson moved with his unit, he took his ivory dice with him and it seemed that this was the end of the 'school'. Fortunately, Captain Downie, the Glaswegian dental officer, came to the rescue; he made up vulcanite cubes and then with his dental drill, cut out the various symbols to produce a splendid inlaid set. One night, on his way back to his *basha*, Downie had the misfortune to lose all the dice through a hole in his pocket. Next morning, after a careful search along the path, only three of the missing dice were recovered. He soon set about making good the deficiency but the two new dice turned out to be of a slightly darker shade. In due course, we found that these new dice would come up with aces 1 in 5 whereas, the original, lighter-coloured dice averaged aces 1 in 10. Eventually we all adjusted ourselves to playing with loaded dice.

Previously, Captain Downie had demonstrated his craftmanship by carrying out a gold inlay for my broken front tooth; it was no mean feat to produce precision work in such primitive conditions. I did not enquire as to the source of the gold but I had an idea that one of his Dental Unit made a point of salvaging the metal before any Jap burial.

Captain Paddy Renaine of the Transfusion Unit was a keen but unlucky liar dice player. Often, when his bluff was called, he would hold his thumb and index finger an inch apart and remark: 'Just that much off!' Early in 1944, after Paddy had received a Jap bullet through his upper arm, the occasion arose for him to be reminded of this favourite remark of his. During the same incident, Downie sustained a bullet wound of the neck. Over a year later, Willie Wilson was evacuated from Burma with pulmonary tuberculosis. Thus three foundation members of the Bawli poker dice school found that the dice were loaded against them.

CHAPTER ELEVEN

On the Move

In Arakan, during the winter months, low humidity and a less powerful sun produced a more tolerable climate. Christmas Day 1943 was cool, quiet and pleasant, the only military activity coming from our dive bombers delivering their gifts to the Japanese. After attending the post-operative dressings, the men of No 7 put on their smartest, cleanest uniforms and following a full inspection parade, joined the personnel of the Field Ambulance on the nearby paddy field. Here entertainment was provided by a band playing recognisable melodies on their tuneful Irish pipes. From the Red Cross and medical supplies there was an issue of chocolate, nuts, cigarettes, beer and spirits. For me the mail brought letters from home together with a welcome parcel of tobacco from Maurice Joseph and Bill Wallace of the 80th. The evening was rounded off by a late poker dice session at the end of which I was richer by five rupees.

The New Year of 1944 found the Japanese still in occupation of Maungdaw, on the Naf estuary and of Buthidaung, east of the Mayo Ridge. They also held the metalled link road which once had carried a railway passing through two tunnels driven through the mountain ridge. On the west of the ridge, guarding the tunnels and the approach to Maungdaw, the Japanese had constructed the formidable and well-concealed fortress of Razabil. The object of the Allied 1944 offensive was to clear the enemy from these positions. The 7th Indian Division was to advance down east of the ridge to take Buthidaung and the 5th Indian Division on the west side was to capture Razabil and Maungdaw. Guarding the eastern flank was the 81st West African Division, aiming to advance southwards down the Kaladon valley. To link the two main forces, the mere mule tracks of Goppe and Maunghnana passes had to be made more substantial and a few miles further south, the Ngakeudauk (Okydoke) area had to be captured to allow this pass to be developed into a military road. The Japanese 55th Division under the command of Major General Sakurai, together with a task force led by Colonel Tanahashi, victor of Arakan in 1943, had rather different plans which became evident in the first week of February 1944.

After some six months of being the only mobile surgical unit in the Arakan, support for No 7 came from two additional MSU's commanded by Major Crawford and Major Lilwall who were attached to field ambulances east of the ridge. Later it was the intention that No 15 MSU commanded by Major Weston should relieve No 7 west of the Ridge and allow our withdrawal for rest and refitting; this plan was changed by the course of events. On New Year's Eve, whilst the British guns and mortars were ranging on Point 124 north of Razabil, No 7 was busily engaged with casualties reaching No 15 CCS at Bawli Bazar. The operating list that night started at 1600 hours and continued throughout the night, to finish with the dawn of 1944. One of the abdominal casualties actually had his operation started in 1943 and finished in 1944; during the operation, it was noticed that someone had stuck a notice on the theatre wall – a drawing of holly and mistletoe surrounded by the words: 'Happy New Year!'

The first fortnight of January saw the unit occupied chiefly at night. During the daylight hours, collection of the wounded would often be prevented by Jap fire and only at dusk did bearer units manage to pick up the casualties. This usually meant a delay of several hours before operative measures could be undertaken and lists not infrequently started at 2000 hours to finish in time for breakfast. During the morning the unit, having paraded for Mepacrine, would be engaged in ward work, dressings and attention to intravenous drips. Each day there was the task of arranging the evacuation of patients fit to travel by road or river.

Whenever possible, lost sleep was made up in the afternoons and it was one of the few remaining luxuries to have a couple of hours of shut-eye on the camp bed without any mosquito netting. This form of rest was popularly known as 'charpoy bashing'.

Whilst so engaged one hot afternoon, I was rudely awakened by a burst of automatic fire through the roof of my *basha*. Soon afterwards, I heard some nearby tittering and so, having slipped out through the side window, I crept round in the bushes to come up behind a couple of unknown combatant officers enjoying their somewhat sick joke. The joke rebounded on them when they were made to drop their weapons and dance to the tune of my revolver directed at their feet. Fortunately no one was hurt and after they had apologised for their stupidity they admitted that. under the influence of rum, they had thought that the escapade would bring some light relief to a hot boring afternoon.

After breakfast on 19th January, No 7 severed its attachment to No 15 CCS. At long last with our own full complement of transport, the unit now could really be entitled to have the prefix 'Mobile' and all members were quite thrilled as our small convoy moved off across the Pruma. The bridge near Bawli had, during the quiet season, received considerable attention from the Royal Engineers and the now solid structure no longer creaked as we again crossed, this time heading south. The mango grove where I had first made contact with the unit many months previously, was soon passed on the right. The journey was uneventful, apart from finding it essential at Briasco Bridge to take over control of our 3-tonner the driver of which had proved himself quite incapable of handling the vehicle. The red, dusty road led in a south-westerly direction through light scrub interspaced with thickets of bamboo, clumps of banana trees and the isolated betel nut palm tree. To the right there were occasional glimpses of the small paddy fields adjoining the deep *chaungs* which thrust their way inland from the Naf estuary.

Before noon, the Main Dressing Station of No 10 Field Ambulance was found east of the road and by 1400 hours the unit set up and was ready to deal with casualties. The location was within a few hundred yards of the thick, dark jungle of the Mayo Ridge from which at times there echoed the odd rifle shot as well as the occasional short rattle of automatic weapon fire. Under the protection of a low, scrub-covered hill, empty *bashas*, with modifications, were soon made available as post-operative wards. The theatre tentage was erected under a large tree, the foliage of which provided a splendid cover from the heat and from prying aircraft. Personal accommodation was in a small camouflaged tent put up over a dug-out on the hillside. It was so arranged that the camp bed was below ground level so that at night there was some protection from any stray bullet that might pass through the tent; as an extra precaution, the tin-hat was propped up behind the pillow. With the increased aerial activity during the day and gunfire at night, the unit needed no encouragement to dig at this or other subsequent sites. Whilst at Bawli, the digging of slit trenches had been a somewhat leisurely affair until one afternoon a squadron of Japanese bombers passed low overhead. No bombs were dropped but it was amazing to see the stimulus that was given to the digging. Within a few hours, the trenches had become major excavations, surpassed only by those at Razabil fortress.

In the days before the Allies had established complete air superiority it was not uncommon to witness dogfights high in the sky. Hurricanes would act as stooges and first engage the Zeros; then lurking Spitfires would swoop down to make the kill. One morning, as I was seated on an elevated latrine, observing the battles going on high above, a rude shock was provided by a couple of Zeros suddenly appearing at tree-top level, roaring towards the Field Ambulance, with guns blazing. Thanks to various forms of dysentery, it was not unusual for urgent visits to be made to the latrines, but it must have been rare for anyone to vacate a latrine at even greater speed, literally with one's pants down. From behind the latrines a clear vision was obtained of the goggled Zero pilots as they swept over without causing a single casualty.

Apart from the enemy activity, the site at Chota Maunghnana was quite pleasant; it had the bonus of palatable drinking water which was an enjoyable change from the chlorinated mawkish water available at our previous locations. During the hot dry season, evaporation through the porous walls of canvas containers hung outside one's tent, was used to create a cooling of the contents. When cooled by this method, the spring water issuing from the Mayo Ridge, produced a most refreshing drink.

Within twelve hours of our arrival, Paddy Renaine joined us with his Field Transfusion Unit whose services were soon required. Amongst the great variety of wounded requiring operation, there was a man whose lower lip, chin and lower jaw had been shot away. We knew that injuries of this type travelled badly as they were unable to swallow fluids during evacuation and on the many miles back to India, heat together with lack of fluid, produced severe dehydration which in some cases proved fatal. In an effort to overcome the difficulty in swallowing, a new method was tried out. After excising damaged tissue and controlling bleeding, a temporary 'jaw' was fashioned from dental 'Stent', a compound which becomes malleable when soaked in boiling water and regains its rigidity when cooled. This splint was fixed in position with silver wire which was twisted round the remaining back molar tooth on each side. The tongue, which tended to fall back, was anchored with thread on to this Stent mandible. Finally, the gap of missing chin and lower lip was bridged by layers of vaseline lint, made up to the normal thickness of the tissues and accurately stitched in position with thread.

With this temporary arrangement, the patient was able to swallow fluid during the rough, hot journey back to base and survived to have a proper reconstruction carried out in a facio-maxillary unit. Unfortunately the supply of Stent was limited; it was not listed amongst our equipment and the discs we had acquired had been donated by a visiting dental unit.

Later, when no Stent was available, an alternative material was sought to provide the temporary jaw. From the Red Cross comforts, a particularly irritating Indian gramophone record was selected; with much difficulty and frustration, using flame heating and strong scissors, the mandibular gap was bridged. Added to the problem of moulding the material, there was failure in the attempt to fix silver wire to vulcanite; eventually we came to the conclusion that a gramophone record was no substitute for 'Stent'.

When there had been a large inflow of casualties, I usually made periodic breaks in the operating list to look over those men awaiting attention and then would decide who might be requiring an earlier visit to the theatre. On one particular afternoon, the reception tent was full and overflowing. Outside, lying on a stretcher in the shade of a large tree, I saw an ill-looking man with his left arm heavily bandaged. His forearm was cold, white and pulseless, the fingers were clawed. Further inspection under the dressings revealed that a tight tourniquet encircled the upper arm. There was no 'T' marked on his forehead and no note had been made as to when this tourniquet had been applied at the Advanced Dressing Station but it was obvious that it had been in position for many hours. The man was quickly brought to the theatre and the tourniquet was removed. On exploring his gun-shot wound, which was a relatively minor one, it was found that the main brachial artery was intact. The original bleeding had come from a small collateral artery and could have been controlled by a pressure dressing. Unfortunately no recovery in the circulation followed removal of the tourniquet and there was no alternative but to carry out an amputation. This example clearly demonstrated that the tourniquet can cause more damage than the original wound. If it has to be applied to check vigorous arterial bleeding, it must be released every half hour and only tightened again if bleeding recurs. It is a true saying that more limbs have been lost than lives saved by the improper use of the tourniquet.

One morning near Chota Maunghnana, Buddy Date, a Canadian fighter pilot, made a crash landing. He had been shooting up ground targets over the Japanese lines and as he banked his Hurricane, he was hit by a rifle bullet fired from the ground. Afterwards he related that he was very nearly compelled to make a forced landing behind the enemy lines but, knowing what his fate would have been, he struggled north for a few miles and brought his plane down on some open ground beside the Field Ambulance. Within a very short time he had been resuscitated and was on the operating table where it was found that omentum (the apron of fat suspended from the stomach) was effectively plugging the entry wound in the lower left chest. The bullet had passed transversely through the body to lodge in the right upper arm. The track had been through the pleura catching next the dome of the diaphragm and then below the heart and pericardium to pass through the liver and out the other side of the trunk. Quite apart from the bullet missing vital structures, the important factor that saved him was the diaphragmatic injury; this had allowed the omentum to come up from the abdomen and block the chest entry wound. If this had not taken place, the pilot would have had an open blowing chest wound which, from mediastinal flapping, could have led to speedy death or landing into Japanese hands with the same end result.

He recovered from the operation but after evacuation to base hospital, he developed an empyema – (collection of pus between the layers of the pleura) for which further drainage was required. We heard that eventually recovery was complete and Buddy Date was back flying again one year after sustaining that unlucky and lucky wound.

Although resuscitation played an all-important role, particularly in the management of chest and abdominal injuries, there were limits as to what could be achieved. A patient whose blood pressure, in spite of intensive measures, could not be brought above a systolic of 100, would be unlikely to survive the operation. Many such cases had sustained severe multiple injuries. Ideally the abdomen was best opened on a rising blood pressure and there was no doubt about the value of continued transfusion during operation. After internal bleeding had been controlled and provided there was no gross faecal contamination of muscle, a steady improvement in the patient's condition was to be expected. It may be ideal for the abdomen to be closed within the hour, but unfortunately intra-abdominal wounds are frequently multiple and it is useless to close that abdomen unless and until all the damage has been attended to. The record of blood pressure and pulse taken every ten minutes gives a clear indication as to how the patient is weathering the operation and should afford a guide as to what measures can safely be adopted. If the individual surgeon gets some idea as to how long he will take to carry out, say, a bowel resection with anastomosis, he can judge how much longer the abdomen will have to be kept open, and if all is not well, he may have to substitute some procedure which deals with the injury more conservatively and speedily.

One of those most lethal types of abdominal wound was encountered soon after we had joined the Field Ambulance. The soldier was admitted a couple of hours after he had been hit in the abdomen by a high velocity bullet. Faecal material was seen to be issuing from the exit wound at the back. At operation it was found that the large bowel on the right had been shattered and in addition to gross contamination of the peritoneum, faeces had been blasted into the muscles of the back. Like all similar cases of this type, he failed to survive in spite of excision, free drainage, local insufflation with sulphathiazole and the introduction of sulphonamides with the intravenous drip. The pulse rate rose steadily uninfluenced by blood transfusion; morphia failed to control the restlessness and the general condition rapidly deteriorated with increasing abdominal distension unrelieved by gastric suction. Death occurred some 48 hours after operation, the clinical features being those of intense toxaemia the result of flooding the circulation with potent poisons coming from the absorption of what was literally an intra-muscular injection of faeces.

After a busy five days with No 10 Field Ambulance, there came the movement order for No 7 to join No 45 Field Ambulance near Zeganbyin, a few miles north of Razabil fortress. It was with regret that we had to part company with Paddy Renaine and his transfusion unit which was required to cross to the eastern side of the Mayo Ridge. At this time, little did we realise what were to be the circumstances of our next meeting.

The operating theatre at Chota Maunghnama

CHAPTER TWELVE

Crisis

On Sunday afternoon, 23rd January 1944, No 7 MSU moved south in two sections. George Quayle got off first at 1500 hours with the heavier equipment (including tentage) and the rest of the unit followed an hour later in the 15 cwt truck and two station wagons. The route passed into more wooded country near the Ngakyedauk Pass which by now had been converted into a dirt road capable of bearing the armour and transport of an invading army. The cutting of the road over the pass had been a feat of engineering by the sappers and miners of the 7th Division. They were proud of their masterpiece on the approach roads to which notices had been erected reading: 'Sweat made this road. Speed will break it!' As our modest convoy passed along there were seen to be groups of coolies engaged in maintenance. Small tins filled with red earth from the verges were used to spread a covering on the surface and this was sprinkled with water. The process was being carried out in a most leisurely manner; as they ambled to and fro on their wide splayed feet, they were certainly not losing any sweat.

The journey was continued through Wabyin which lay just west of the Ngakyedauk Pass. Further south the road narrowed through thicker jungle and sometimes it was difficult to decide, on reaching a fork, which route should be taken. It was with relief that we reached our destination before sundown. The No 45 Field Ambulance was located near Zeganbyin on an area of open ground between hillocks covered with scrub and thick foliage, the whole area being overshadowed by the dark jungle which climbed the slopes of the nearby Mayo Ridge.

The evening meal was taken with the Field Ambulance officers whose mess was an awning slung under the cover of a large tree.

This tree was hollow and the excavated lower end made an excellent fireplace in which logs blazed to give brightness and warmth without attracting undue attention, the smoke being dispersed amongst the foliage. Before retiring we had a visit from Captain Stafford whose bearer unit had been collecting a few minor casualties. He told us that there was increased Japanese activity along the ridge but the general view was that this information was exaggerated. He refused to join us round the dimly-lit mess table which he insisted was well within sniper range from the ridge.

Apart from sporadic gun-fire, the night was uneventful and at first light, we set about digging out from a hillock slope to give a protected area for the dyed theatre tentage which was draped with foliage to blend with the surroundings. Since there were no major cases to be dealt with, the unit could concentrate on completing various refinements to the theatre block. It was soon obvious that the Razabil fortress was receiving considerable attention from a battery of heavy artillery just north of the Field Ambulance. One particular gun produced a peculiar cracking sound and from this regular distinctive noise we could appreciate how hard the gunners were working to maintain the constant barrage of shells passing over our heads.

Twice during that day, there was the clear sight of bombs leaving our Vengeance dive bombers before they straightened out to weave away at tree-top level. That night many Lee tanks roared past and soon were adding their fire directly into the foxhole openings of the fortress. Although it was thought that the defences of Razabil had been flattened, the Japanese bunker system remained substantially intact and from the labyrinth of underground tunnels the enemy was ready to strike back at our advancing troops. This resulted in No 7 being fully occupied with many casualties, mainly with grenade and bullet wounds. The next day, to reinforce the pounding from artillery, dive bombers and tanks, a large force of Liberator bombers delivered their contribution which was scattered over a wide area and added some civilian casualties to swell the overloaded operating lists.

For the next forty-eight hours, there was little time for food or rest and when daytime work eased, night sessions continued. At this stage, our autoclave broke down and we urgently had to obtain a replacement. Subidhar Karem Singh made an early start in the station wagon and was able to get through to the forward hospital at Dhuapolong when no spare could be found in Bawli Bazar. Without any hesitation, Colonel Eames of the 125 IGH agreed to part with an autoclave and Karem Singh returned with it twenty-four hours later after an uneventful journey. During his absence, we relied upon the sterilising facilities provided by the Field Ambulance.

On 30th January, we were joined by No 15 MSU, commanded by Major Weston, who had been ordered to relieve and replace No 7 to give us a rest; circumstances prevented this order being carried out. Major Bill Weston, of stubby build, was an entertaining extrovert who, before studying medicine, had had many occupations, mainly in the United States. He had been a schoolmaster, a cattle man, a demolition expert and a beauty parlour employee; his recounting of how his various jobs always ended in disaster, provided amusing and fascinating stories. His main interests, apart from surgery, were bird watching and food. The latter hobby sustained a sad blow on his journey south when at 1400 hours he called to see Brigadier Meneces at Bawli Bazar. Since he had missed his breakfast Bill had hoped to get a meal at Bawli but the Brigadier greeted him with:

'Don't wait for lunch, my boy; you had better press on to find No 7 before sundown.'

He did reach us just before dark and even whilst having a large evening meal, he continued to bemoan the missed breakfast and lunch. This was the first time that I heard his oft repeated observation that some happening was 'like Josephine Baker's left tit', neither right nor fair!

No 7 continued to function at full pressure whilst No 15 got its theatre tentage put up in a hollow on the other side of our little hillock. Bill was soon ready to try out his new theatre with what he considered to be an acute appendix. This turned out to be a non-acute high retro-caecal appendix which was removed with some difficulty. It was demonstrated to him that, in Arakan, abdominal symptoms were more likely to be due to malaria than acute appendicitis. His next incision was accidental; in order to get camouflage material to cover his tents, using a *dhar*, he started slashing down bamboo; unfortunately the weapon continued through the bamboo to open Bill's left knee joint. After his wound had been cleaned and stitched, 'Private Ward' accommodation was found in the vacant mortuary tent. No infection developed but by the time the knee was fit for full duty, the military situation had so changed that No 7 had to remain to work alongside No 15.

Bill Weston, after acquiring his Fellowship, had interested himself in orthopaedic surgery so that, although well able to cope with limb injuries, he lacked experience in abdominal surgery. Until he brought his unit into the Arakan, he had had little opportunity to deal with trunk injuries from missiles and he had not appreciated to what extent the climate, disease and the jungle would make him modify his ideas. He did however realise that in limb injuries, dead and devitalised muscle must be excised, skin should be saved, tissue tension had to be relieved by opening up haematomata (collections of blood), skin closure was to be avoided, wounds were not to be packed with vaseline gauze and before evacuation, plasters needed splitting. Soon after his knee injury and before he was fit to work again, he asked me to give him a crash course on the management of abdominal wounds in jungle warfare. Sitting together on the hillock between our theatre tents, I showed him the methods used for carrying out a quick anastomosis (joining up bowel to restore continuity) and for this we had an adequate supply of intestines from corpses but the heat, the smell and the flies tended to shorten the duration of these sewing lessons.

To Bill it needed to be pointed out that even a minute mortar fragment entry wound over the abdomen needed to be carefully explored as not infrequently it was found that an apparently insignificant puncture led down to perforated bowel. In hospital, X-rays and observation for a few hours might be useful in deciding whether or not an abdomen should be opened but in field conditions, doubtful cases should be submitted to early exploration. Such patients were usually not desperately ill and were none the worse for a 'look-see' policy; on occasions the finding of perforations amply justifies the operation.

Bill was under the impression that in order to get an adequate exposure of the abdominal contents, he should slit the abdomen from breast-bone to pubis. I pointed out to him that rarely was such an incision justifiable. The position of the entry and exit wounds, together with the physical signs frequently gave the clue as to whether the upper or lower abdomen demanded attention. The vertical incision to just below or just above the navel was commonly all that was required. If, on opening the abdomen, the preliminary inspection revealed that spleen or kidney might be involved, a transverse division of muscle combined with adequate mobilisation of the damaged organ, gave good exposure.

The thoraco-abdominal cases often presented a problem for newcomers. Where there was a large chest wound, it was obvious that this should first receive attention to give an air-tight closure before opening the abdomen. A small chest wound and signs of intra-abdominal trouble might tempt a surgeon to delay attending to the chest until after the abdomen had been sorted out. Bitter experience led me to conclude that a small chest wound is best cleaned and dressed first and then the abdominal condition should be tackled. The patient's condition quickly deteriorates if, after an extensive abdominal operation, he has to be turned on his face to allow attention to the chest.

It needed to be pointed out that once the abdomen is opened, the first object is to locate and control any source of profuse haemorrhage; bleeding is liable to show increased activity as the result of transfusion and exploration. A common source of haemorrhage is the jejunum (upper part of the small bowel), a few perforations of which can soon result in an abdominal cavity full of blood. Quite frequently, the semi-dilated damaged portion of the small bowel presented on opening the abdomen; temporary occlusion should be made whilst a rapid but systematic examination of the remainder of the abdominal contents was carried out. Sometimes during this inspection, foreign bodies were found lying free; if they were not located at this time, no special search should be made for them. It was advised that the surgeon should get a complete picture of the total damage before starting any repairs. The closure of multiple perforations can be more time-consuming than a resection of a damaged loop; in addition, post-operatively, local reactive swelling at the site of many repairs is liable to cause more interference with the re-establishment of waves of contraction than removal of a large loop of bowel to include the perforations.

In addition to advising on the use of the colostomy for wounds of the large bowel, the need for drainage in all cases and stressing the advantages to be gained by delayed closure of abdominal wounds, many other points of surgical technique were fully aired. Before he was called upon to deal with abdominal casualties, initially I had Bill to assist me and then the roles were reversed until he could safely tackle the problems on his own.

When both units were working all out with very little chance of a rest, so much time had to be spent in the theatre that the post-operative care of patients became a problem. We had heard that there were nursing sisters at Bawli Bazar and a hope was expressed that they might, during daylight hours, be brought forward to help. This request, fortunately as it turned out, was not allowed since Higher Authority considered that it was inadvisable to expose sisters to the risk of capture by the Japanese. As an alternative, we were able to get some part-time assistance from Captain Stafford and from the personnel of the Field Ambulance who gave valuable service in looking after post-operative drips and suctions.

The news drifted through that, on 4th February, Tong Bazar, east of the Goppe Pass, had been taken by the Japanese but it was several days later before we became fully aware of the seriousness of the situation. A trip north was made on 6th February to liaise with a newly established CCS just south of Briasco Bridge. Various problems had to be discussed in connection with the evacuation of our post-operative patients. This CCS was a fresh arrival in the Arakan and the personnel expressed some concern about the developing situation as through field glasses they spotted figures moving along the ridge. Incorrectly as it turned out, I re-assured their general duties officer Major Egan that these troops must be ours as I could see one had a beard. It was suggested that I might prolong my visit to give their surgical specialist, Vause Gregg, a hand with his list and an additional inducement to stay was an invitation to an outdoor cinema show that evening. I had to refuse and pointed out that I must rejoin my own unit before sundown. It is not recorded whether or not any Japanese actually tried to attend the cinema show, but early next morning, the CCS had to make a hasty withdrawal to Bawli Bazar before a Jap force came over the Maunghnama Pass to cut the road at Briasco Bridge.

On arrival back at Zeganbyin, there was found to be increased activity in all directions. The battery, which previously had been directing its full attention against Razabil, had turned some of its guns to fire in the opposite direction. This change produced an unfortunate accident in which one of the newly positioned guns failed to clear the parapet, resulting in a premature explosion of the shell. A gunner had the muscles of the left side of his abdominal wall blown away and yet the peritoneum remained intact. It was found that he had sustained considerable intra-abdominal blast injury; a pulped spleen had to be removed and repairs were required for a torn pancreas and for mesenteric lacerations. In spite of all our efforts, this patient's condition steadily deteriorated and with a temperature of 105 died some hours after operation.

Brigadier Meneces visited us and, as far as possible, put us in the picture. He reported on the events east of the Ngakyedauk Pass and there was particular reference to our colleagues of No 66 Field Ambulance and of No 12 MSU who had been overrun by the Japanese. We were advised to evacuate back our personal kit and spare equipment; No 7 and No 15 MSU's were to combine to give a constant operative service. We moved our camp beds into dug-outs in the bushes and arranged that, if need be, we could make a speedy exit through the back of the tent into thick scrub. Just in case it became necessary to find our individual ways to the west, each had his haversack ready packed with his own particular preferences. Mine contained personal documents and records together with a map, a full water bottle, sterilisation tablets, Mepacrine tablets and a clean pair of socks.

During the day, from both sides, aerial activity was considerable but movement on the ground was not unduly restricted. In order to get transport repairs carried out, a visit to workshops at Bawli Bazar was required. George Quayle undertook the trip north with the faulty vehicles. On the return journey, the small convoy had been machine-gunned from the air and a dash was required along one section of road under mortar fire. No casualties were sustained apart from Banzi who, through disobeying orders, received his cut leg and lacerated trousers. Of an evening, 'Tokyo Rose', in her honey-voiced broadcasts, was informing us and the world, that the glorious Imperial Japanese Army had wiped out the 7th Indian

Division and was mopping up the scattered remnants of the 5th Division (that was us) before continuing their victorious advance into India. About the same time, officers commanding all units, both large and small, received the message from Supreme Commander, Lord Louis Mountbatten: 'Hold on. There must be no withdrawal. You are making history.'

Early in February 1944, the large scale plan of the Japanese High Command, known as Operation C, was put into action. The object of this plan was to invade India from Arakan. It was to be done by splitting open the British front, sealing off the eastern half from the western half and cutting the lines of communications of both. Each sector was to be destroyed and the road to Chittagong laid open for the Japanese army. The Tanahashi force met with initial success by blocking the Ngakyedauk Pass and east of the pass, pinning down the 7th Division into what became known as the 'Admin Box'. The whole of 'C' plan was to have been completed by 10th February, but the Japanese commander had left out of his reckoning the stubborn resistance he was to encounter. He had also forgotten air power. From captured documents, all the details of the Japanese plan were known to the Allies but even so the enemy rigidly adhered to the original plan and failed to adjust to the changing circumstances.

The dawn of 10th February was cool and still, with clumps of bamboos standing ramrod-stiff above the grey, wreathing mist. It was still very early when we received warning that there was likely to be an attack that night, and most of the day was occupied with our preparations. Ringing the area, a series of trenches were dug and arrangements were made for the perimeter defences to be manned by the three companies of the Field Ambulance, the two mobile units and a mule company. Our unit was issued with rifles, ammunition and one Sten gun, the latter being handed to George Quayle who was the least likely to bump it into accidental automatic firing. No.7 Indian Mobile Surgical Unit, on parade in their new role, could hardly be regarded as a first class fighting force; in fact, their ludicrous appearance would have been laughable, had the situation not been so serious. The theatre tents were completely smothered in fresh foliage and along the adjacent scrub-covered slope a series of slit trenches were excavated. At sundown, all personnel were on the alert and settled in the trenches from which it would be possible to direct fire across 50 yards of open ground. The thought did not fail to cross our minds that this was a rather strange situation; here was a medical unit all set to kill or maim the enemy, but after the action, provided we survived, it might be necessary for the same unit to get to work to repair the damage it had itself inflicted.

In the earlier part of the night, soon after settling on the right flank of the defences, a message was received that a badly wounded man had arrived in reception. I had to collect Corporal Cross and go along the line of trenches to tell all members of the Unit that they might be required and, at the same time, impressing on them that when I returned they were to keep their fingers off the triggers. Whilst Cross dug up the pannier of instruments to start sterilisation and preparation of the theatre, all efforts were being made to bring the patient into a state fit for anaesthetic and operation. The casualty, who had a severely shattered thigh as well as intra-abdominal injuries, was in marked shock which did not respond to treatment. He failed to survive beyond half an hour, so the theatre preparations were cancelled and the instruments were re-buried.

With a shaded torch I groped my way back to the trench on the right flank without attracting any fire from the unit. My companions in the trench were a nursing sepoy, the water carrier and sweeper Nanoo; there was no room to stretch our legs and it was difficult to find a comfortable position. On this bitterly cold night, the clear sky showed up the brilliance of the stars and although there was sporadic gun-fire, the rising moon did not bring the expected attack. As the night wore on, Nanoo had to be wakened at intervals to bring a halt to his loudly echoing snores. Just before the misty dawn war cries in the form of jackal calls heralded the Japanese attack and with it came an outburst of sustained rifle and mortar fire. The unit was then fully alert and ready to shoot at anything that might appear in the clearing covered by our positions. The sounds of the main engagement came from the other side of a hillock on the left flank and, the din made it evident that the section defended by the mule company was involved. It was later learned that the Japanese attack had been driven off, partly by the fire from the company and partly by the confusion created by stampeding mules.

With the advance of daylight, I had hoped to get some sleep but this was not possible because of many minor interruptions and there was no alternative but to get up and about. During the morning the trenches were enlarged to allow room for stretchers and blankets in the hope that the next night might be made more comfortable than the previous one. When all was quiet after dark, a rifle shot rang out from the position of the Field Ambulance's 'A' company. The shot was followed by some loud oaths and then, after a short pause, a more prolonged stream of cursing rent the silent night. In the morning the explanation was forthcoming. I gathered that the QM had ordered a sepoy who was standing on the parapet to get down into the trench at once. As the man jumped down he pulled the trigger of his rifle to send a bullet whistling past the QM's ear. Having been thoroughly told off for his carelessness, the unfortunate sepoy, turning in the cramped space, accidentally pricked the QM's buttock with his bayonet. This incident produced the second burst of abuse.

During the night there were periods of machine-gun and mortar fire, but no attack came our way and it was possible, in turns, to get some sleep. At dawn, it was discovered that nearby combatant units had vanished in the night. Such an event was not unusual; a field ambulance would, for protection, settle beside a fighting unit which might move on without a word to leave a 'defenceless' medical unit on its own. During those nights of confusion, some medical units could take good care of themselves and there was at least one occasion when, in the darkness, a British patrol was driven off by the fire from a field Ambulance.

On 12th February, in company with the Field Ambulance and No 15 MSU we were glad to move several miles to the north into a more protected site, inside the brigade box, near the foot of the Ngakyedauk Pass.

CHAPTER THIRTEEN

Okydoke

The new site selected was on the westside of a tree-covered hillock which gave protection from the immediate neighbourhood of the Ngakyedauk Pass. As before, the theatre tentage was put up over a platform dug out from the slope. Our own small tents, on the hill above the theatre, covered beds sunk into slit trenches. That night there was a 'Stand to' and those of us allocated a night's rest were awakened by the visit of a Jap bomber dropping its load across the Field Ambulance area. The nearest crater was thirty yards from the theatre and the blast of the explosion, produced quite a movement of the camp bed even although it was below ground level. There were a few casualties and this meant early activity for Bill Weston who was first on call. The new arrangement of two mobile units working together proved most satisfactory, as it usually meant that a surgeon could work all night knowing that the following night there were prospects for some sleep.

During the next morning, I was called to see a brigadier suffering from severe lumbago and sciatica. He was most concerned that the pain was preventing him from concentrating on the attack that was to be made to clear the Pass. This situation was in a way similar to the one said to have confronted Napoleon before and during the battle of Waterloo, when he was experiencing thrombophlebitis in prolapsed haemorrhoids (an attack of piles). The discomfort and pain rendered Napoleon incapable of making decisions and probably played an important part in his defeat. Injections of local anaesthetic brought some relief to the brigadier, but he was not called upon to make the crucial attack; the assault went in next day under the command of his replacement.

The week that followed saw both No 7 and No 15 working round the clock; during the short breaks, we had good views of the Vengeances dive bombing the approaches to the Ngakyedauk Pass. These attacks and the artillery barrage would periodically cease to allow the slow low-flying Dakotas to drop supply parachutes east of the pass.

About this time, a message was received from Brigadier John Bruce, now Consulting Surgeon 14th Army, that he was at Bawli Bazar and he would wait there for a week in the hope that I might be able to get back to see him. He did not report to HQ India that he was staying the extra week and it was assumed that he had been captured or killed. A very impressive memorial service was held in Poona for him. He turned up ten days later! Once the Jap brigade had been cleared from the Briasco Bridge area, the journey back was made without difficulty and at Bawli I was able to discuss surgical problems with Brigadiers Bruce and Grant Massie.

It was decided that, in future, mobile surgical units should abandon the use of the thoraco-brachial plaster and change to a plaster which kept the wounded arm fixed to the chest; this method would enable a man with a shoulder injury to be better fitted into an ambulance and lessen his discomfort during evacuation. Forward units were to receive instructions that they were not to pack wounds with lengths of vaseline gauze which tended to act as a plug and encouraged infective complications. It was confirmed that a severely shocked casualty should not be held at the ADS (Advanced Dressing Station) just to allow resuscitation. By the time such a patient reached the Mobile Unit at the MDS (Main Dressing Station) a few hours later, he had by then relapsed again into severe shock and a second intensive resuscitation often was not successful. On several occasions, it had been noted that a badly wounded man when picked up might be given a subcutaneous injection of morphia gr. ½ and then, if he was still in pain at the ADS, a further gr. ½ might be added. On reaching the Surgical Unit at the MDS resuscitation would sweep the morphia into the general circulation and the patient would need to be treated for morphia overdosage before operation could be undertaken. It was advised that, in future, a smaller dose of morphia should be given, not under the skin but intravenously, thus bringing quick relief and avoiding the risk of overdosage.

My fleeting visit to Bawli Bazar made a pleasant break from the violence of the battles raging some ten miles to the south. The Queen Alexandra nursing sisters attached to the CCS seemed to bring a touch of civilisation to the Arakan into which previously, no female had been allowed to venture. On a paddy field after sundown, a mobile open-air cinema showed a film featuring Ginger Rogers. There followed a personal appearance by 'Stainless Stephen' whose brilliant solo performance kept everyone highly entertained for over an hour. Many will remember this Sheffield-born comedian from the days before the war when he delivered his patter interspaced with commas, semi-colons and full stops. He was one of the few show biz personalities who ventured to forward areas within the sound of gun-fire. I well recall his topical story of his jeep journey into Arakan when odd groups of soldiers unsuccessfully tried to thumb a lift. 'Stainless' remarked:

'I was pleased to see that the refusal to stop was taken in good spirit and they all gave me the "V" for victory sign (semi-colon); the only thing that puzzled me was the upward and circular motion they gave to the gesture (full stop)!'

After the show, on the way to the Mess tent, I was walking with 'Stainless' on whose other side was a rather diminutive sister who was chatting away merrily. After some quip from the comedian, the sister retorted:

'Stainless, you are only talking to me like that because I am small.'

Like a shot came the reply:

'Small, my dear! I did not consider you to be small; just thought you were walking in a slit trench!'

Back at Wabyin, both surgical units continued day and night operating whilst the battle of the Ngakyedauk Pass was fought and won by the Allies. General Slim recorded that this battle was of far greater importance than might at first appear; it marked the turning point in the war in South-East Asia and it was the first time that the Japanese failed in their tactics. The outcome of the battle was of immense importance psychologically as it showed that there was an answer to the enemy's infiltrating and enveloping

Supplies dropped by air to forward units

tactics, hitherto invariably successful. Now the Allied troops had confidence in their leaders and in their own ability to defeat the Japanese in the jungle.

By 23rd February the pass was secured and the following day 500 casualties from Sinzweya and the 'Admin Box', were evacuated over Ngakyedauk. Before continuing their journey northwards, the wounded were rested to allow refreshment and the inspection of dressings. We heard first-hand stories of the Japanese atrocities when the Field Ambulances and Mobile Units were over-run. Half a dozen Indian Medical Officers had been herded into a tent and shot through the head. One bullet missed its target and the surviving officer, Lieutenant Basu, covered in the blood and brains of his colleagues, feigned death, later to escape and tell the tale. On MDS hill, during the siege, Majors Lilwall and Crawford had borne the brunt of the surgical work. Many of their patients and orderlies were murdered in cold blood. From No 12 MSU, the Subidhar and several nursing sepoys were killed and Crawford lost the greater part of his unit. Paddy Renaine's transfusion unit was practically wiped out, his men having had their thighs broken before being shot. Paddy himself was wounded in the upper arm, the bullet passing through without damaging the humerus, the brachial artery or the radial nerve. As George Quayle and I, separately inspected the wounded laid out under the shade of the trees, we came on Paddy. We both greeted him with his favourite remark at dice:

'Just that much off!'

Paddy's story was linked with that of Downie the dentist as, during the Jap infiltration, they both sought refuge in the same 3-ton truck. On peeping out from the back of the truck they spotted, in the moonlight, an enemy patrol approaching. They decided to make a dash for it and began to run up a clearing in the jungle. Downie first was hit by a bullet through the neck and he rolled over into the bushes. He cautiously peered out to watch the progress of Paddy who, by then, had reached the top of the hill. He saw the Jap take aim and fire. Paddy was toppled into the undergrowth. Both Paddy and Downie, after lying low for some hours, were able to crawl to where they could get surgical attention. In the case of Downie the bullet had missed the great vessels of the neck but had damaged the hypoglossal nerve. This injury prevented the free mobility of his tongue and thereafter he was unable properly to articulate his frequent, favourite, four letter swear word.

For a week after the battle of the Ngakyedauk Pass, there was a temporary lull in the fighting and no more than half a dozen casualties required operation. The opportunity was taken to make another trip back to Bawli, this time to liaise with Willie Wilson, surgical specialist at No 15 CCS. After lunch, Willie suggested that I might give him some assistance with a bad case of gas gangrene for which he proposed to carry out a disarticulation at the hip. He had cut through the grossly infected brick-red muscle and as he swept round with the amputation knife, the point went through the palm of my left hand. At this stage, I lost interest in the operation which Willie completed on his own. Meantime, I removed my rubber glove filled with my own blood and by pressure encouraged further bleeding from the wound which was then cleaned up and dressed. Before leaving the CCS, I received 15 c.cs of anti-gas gangrene serum into each buttock. The buttock injections gave me a most uncomfortable night but the palm wound gave no trouble and it healed without any complication. Bill Weston covered the work for 48 hours and after that we got back to the usual shift system.

Over many months, we had been asking that efforts should be made to arrange an air evacuation for those casualties unfit to travel by ambulance. Early in March, word came through that, at last, a couple of suitable planes were available and we should have two stretcher cases ready for noon on the 5th. An ambulance was loaded with a 6-day old thoraco-abdominal wound and a second day thigh amputation, to make the short trip to a marked-out paddy field just west of Wabyin. After waiting all afternoon, two planes were eventually seen circling near the Mayo Ridge. As they widened their search, in due course they moved more to the west and at last our flag-waving caught their attention. The planes were high-wing monoplanes, each with room for a single stretcher to be fitted in just behind the pilot. Our patients were quickly transferred from ambulance to plane and the safety straps fixed. In turn, each pilot showed his skill in getting his plane airborne from about a hundred yards of paddy field and just clearing the palm trees at the end of the strip. This was the first time that such an evacuation was achieved west of the Mayo Ridge.

The lull in the fighting did not last for long. Counter attacks by the Japanese south of the Pass produced a steady stream of wounded requiring nightly operating by both surgical units. On 6th March Lieutenant-Colonel Sayers (pathology) and Major Ellis (transfusion service) from Headquarters India, paid a visit to get some impression of forward work, conditions and problems. On the grounds that it was likely that they would see some action after dark, we persuaded them to stay the night. Neither they, nor we, expected such a night; all hell was let loose. The darkness was illuminated by many fires on the slopes of the Mayo Ridge and for hours on end there was no let-up in the mortar and automatic fire mixed with bombing and artillery fire.

This activity of course was followed by a flood of casualties which kept us and our visitors busy throughout the night. Amongst those with abdominal wounds, was a corporal who had sustained a bullet wound which had lacerated the small bowel, perforated the stomach, duodenum and gallbladder and finally had fissured the liver. This patient, along with other post-operative cases, required an emergency evacuation the next day. Major Ellis accompanied the convoy on its journey north and he was able to supply constant highly skilled resuscitation for those gravely ill men. After a stormy time, the corporal eventually made a complete recovery but one of the abdominal wounded, moved within four hours of the end of his operation, failed to survive after eight hours of bumping back to the CCS.

CHAPTER FOURTEEN

Maungdaw at Last

At Wabyin, on 7th March, there came a general parting. The convoy of wounded was dispatched on its way towards the north, No 15 MSU left towards the south, the combatant units and Field Ambulance had moved during the night and No 7 MSU was ordered to a new location near Hathipauk. I left the Ngakyedauk area in the station wagon soon after dawn to reconnoitre the map reference given and the unit meantime was to strike tents and pack. As I drove down the jungle trail, fires were still burning on the slopes of the Mayo Ridge but elsewhere there were no signs of activity. After turning right on to an elevated section of the Maungdaw-Buthidaung road, I observed groups of Indian troops, their tin-hats wreathed in foliage, crawling through the bushes on each side of the road. We paid no attention to each other and I thought that they were engaged in an early morning training exercise. This thought was quickly dispelled when mortar shells began to fall on all sides. This activity produced the stimulation for a speedy but rattling passage along the remainder of this section.

On reaching my destination, I was told that half an hour previously the road had been in Jap hands and that possession of it had just been regained by a counter-attack. I could not refrain from strongly expressing the opinion that military police should have been on duty to stop all traffic. It also seemed strange that the Indian troops never raised a finger to warn me that to drive along the exposed section was tempting providence, but no doubt they thought that it was none of their business to interfere with the actions of a fool.

Having decided upon the lay-out at the new location, I made an uneventful return trip to Wabyin to find No 7 all packed and ready to move. Our small convoy then traversed the now firmly held section of road without incident and by noon we linked up with No 58 Field Ambulance. At the new site, there was no convenient hillock into which to dig and the theatre tentage was pitched under mango trees, the trunks of which bore recent bullet marks. The other tents were scattered in bushes around the grove which unfortunately was not at the fruit producing stage. After the fly-proof netting had been put up in the theatre, we found that dust from the near-by road created a problem until the offending section was covered with wet foliage. This was frequently changed and watered by sepoys from the Field Ambulance. At dusk there was the usual 'stand to' but no direct attacks developed. That night we heard an explosion in a nearby artillery unit and although no resulting casualties came our way, the unit remained on alert for an hour after gunfire ceased. Next morning there came the explanation for the disturbance; a Jap patrol had thumbed a lift from a small convoy of Indian gunners who, thinking the hitch-hikers were Gurkhas, had indicated that there was room in the last truck. The journey proceeded through the defences into a Royal Artillery battery where one gun was blown up before the deception was discovered and the intruders dealt with.

The unit soon settled down to routine work which was not unduly arduous. Amongst the admissions was a sepoy who had sustained an abdominal wound from a mortar fragment. At operation, a single minute perforation of small bowel was easily closed. Although the injury was minimal, the post-operative course was stormy on the account of the development of paralytic ileus (paralysis of the small bowel) which proved most resistant to our efforts. Intravenous drip, gastric suction and morphia were continued for a week without any results from enemata. Various additions were made to the drip and even a spinal anaesthetic was given since this sometimes stimulates a bowel action. The abdomen remained distended without any bowel sounds so, as a last resort, I carried out an enterostomy (brought the distended loop to the surface and drained). Following this, the bowel recovered its tone, the distension disappeared, the bowels moved and the man's condition rapidly improved. He was evacuated with the enterostomy draining on the surface.

Some fifteen years after the war, when I was visiting Edinburgh, I joined John Bruce (by now Professor) on one of his teaching rounds. He was talking on the use of gastric suction and drip for paralytic ileus and then, out of the blue, with a twinkle in his eye, brought me into the discussion with:

'That Indian on whom you did an enterostomy in Arakan would not have needed it if you had kept on with drip and suction for a few more days. At base hospital, they had a hell of a job getting the enterostomy closed!'

Naturally this stimulated one of those friendly arguments which he enjoyed and which went on for some time, much to the amusement of the students.

After several days, there was news of considerable activity in the region of the Tunnels through the Mayo Ridge and although we were warned to expect casualties, none arrived. A trip was made to Maungdaw to see the ADMS (5th Div.) to whom I made the suggestion that No 7 might be moved to the Tunnel area, but he decided that we should stay put. One afternoon, Major Cooper of No 13 MSU new to Arakan, paid us a visit and told us that his unit was sited at Wabyin where he had discovered a splendid location, a cut-out hillside, on which to pitch his theatre tentage; it was strange coincidence that he should have picked on the same site that No 7 had sweated on to make, several weeks before.

Our quiet spell continued for a few more days and we even recommenced volley-ball matches before sundown. On the morning of 23rd March there was the first 'mango' shower and with it there arrived the ADMS of 25th Division. He reported that the Japs had broken through from the south and were launching attacks on Maungdaw. We were ordered to move with a light section and as quickly as possible link up with No 15 MSU at Gynapara, North Island. So, leaving behind Subidhar Karem Singh with six men to follow when packing was complete, we set off in the station wagon accompanied by the three tonner. By 1500 hours we had joined forces with No 58 Field Ambulance and once again became associated with Bill Weston's unit.

Throughout that night both surgical units were working all out on a constant stream of casualties. Amongst the wounded, there was a soldier who had been hit in the chest by a sniper's bullet.

The range had been such that the bullet in its flight was spinning without any lateral wobble. The entry wound was through the 6th intercostal space near the right nipple and the exit behind was just clear of the scapula. The entry and exit wounds were no more than ¼" in diameter and they had sealed themselves. Vital structures had been missed and the resulting haemothorax did not recur after a few aspirations. This clean 'through and through', could be regarded as an ideal type of trunk wound, but the effects would have been vastly different had the bullet struck any part of the rib cage. After dealing with several wounds of this type, I was always impressed by the minimal disturbance to the patient and his speedy recovery following chest aspirations to draw off the bloody fluid from the pleural cavity allowing gradual re-expansion of the lung.

In the world of the cinema, the hero invariably gets shot in the region of the left shoulder; a wound in this area could be quite serious and if he were lucky enough not to die from great vessel haemorrhage, damage to the large nerve network (brachial plexus) could leave him with a permanently useless arm. For the film hero, the ideal type of wound would appear to be a clean 'through and through', just outside and below the right nipple.

Whilst on the subject of films, particularly those supposed to have been made on location in Burma, I cannot omit from mention a simple error which, with proper advice, could have been avoided. In one particular film, *The Purple Plain* featuring Gregory Peck, there was a scene of a Burmese village on fire and although the flames crackled merrily, there were no accompaniments. Anyone who has witnessed a bamboo *basha* on fire is impressed by the many violent explosions which result from air pockets in the bamboo suddenly expanding and bursting with loud bangs. Another example of lack of authenticity in a film was pointed out by Colonel Jack Eames. He had been commanding officer of the 125 IGH when I had taken over the surgical division there in 1944. At a chance meeting with him after the war, he was strongly expressing his annoyance over the film *Hasty Heart* which featured Richard Todd. The Colonel had been asked to act as medical adviser to give accurate details of a forward hospital in Burma; he had carefully explained the construction and lay-out of the bamboo wards, where the beds were sited and how the mosquito nets were draped

A mule leader bringing up supplies

Clearing a Japanese foxhole after capture

to find that all his advice was completely ignored by the film director who created a set from his own imagination.

That night we admitted an officer who required an above-knee amputation for gas gangrene which had become established only six hours after the wounding. He was a member of a Commando Unit engaged on a raid south of Maungdaw and had sustained a perforating bullet wound just below the knee joint, both tibial vessels had been destroyed, thus cutting off the blood supply to the limb lower down. The action had taken place on a cultivated paddy field so that Bacillus Welchii, which is present in manure, had been introduced through the wound into the devitalised muscle. This muscle provided an ideal medium for the rapid development of this dangerous spreading infection and it was fortunate that it was possible to carry out amputation through healthy tissues at a higher level. In muscle wounds sustained in uncultivated jungle, the incidence of gas gangrene was low.

Another 'Killer' lurking in agricultural land is the Tetanus Bacillus which is responsible for 'lockjaw'. This bacillus, a normal inhabitant of the intestinal tract of domestic animals, is present in the manure they produce. Although many wounds were sustained in the paddy fields near Maungdaw, I neither saw nor heard of any casualty developing tetanus. An important factor in the low incidence of this infection in these circumstances no doubt was the routine active immunisation. Before soldiers went on active service, it was the policy that they should be given injections of tetanus toxoid at the same time as they received their TAB (anti-typhoid) inoculations. In 1945 at the 14th Army Penicillin Research centre, six patients with tetanus were admitted; this was the total who developed the disease during the push from Mandalay to Rangoon. Four of the patients were Japanese for whom there had been no prophylactic inoculations; one Indian and one African had failed to get their tetanus toxoid injections. The only survivor was African Koloko Billie who was treated with penicillin, anti-tetanic serum, sedation and other measures. At the height of the disease when he was having the severe general muscular spasms, the venous pressure increased to such an extent that the intravenous drip ceased to flow and blood welled up into the drip chamber several feet above the level of the patient. After the acute phase had been controlled, post-tetanic general muscular rigidity persisted for a time; during this stage, Koloko decided to get up and tried to stand beside his bed. He had no control of his rigid body which, at attention, fell backwards to hit the floor like a felled tree. Fortunately he sustained no injury and after this experience, until recovery was complete, he heeded the instructions which were given to him.

Throughout the campaign, amputations for gross injuries to the limbs were not infrequently required. Early in the War, the so-called guillotine type of amputation had been employed, but this had the disadvantage of leaving a raw conical stump which required a higher amputation at the base hospital. In Arakan, it was usual to fashion flaps but no attempt was made to close the stump which was kept open by the insertion of vaseline lint; later, at base, adjustments to retracted skin flaps would be required. In order to avoid flap retraction during evacuation, we tried out a modification which proved satisfactory. Having cut the flaps and removed the limb, long thread sutures were temporarily inserted to hold the flaps forward over the bone end whilst the first dressings were applied; then these stitches were withdrawn before encasing the stump in plaster. Such stumps had adequate drainage, there were no serious infective complications and some, when the dressings were first taken down at base, were found to be well healed.

On North Island, which was linked to Maungdaw by a small bridge, nearby action meant long nocturnal lists for both surgical units. When activity ceased both outside and inside the theatre, one retired hopefully to catch up on lost sleep. The camp bed was sunk in a slit trench the surrounds of which had been built up by sandbags filled with earth. For me, the smell of the damp earth soon produced bronchial spasm which made breathing difficult; relief was eventually obtained after taking Ephedrine which fortunately was available from the dispensary of the Field Ambulance. It was not until many years later that I found that I was allergic to Streptomycin and when ever this antibiotic was used for insufflation into operation wounds, I developed bronchial spasm. It was after the War that the antibiotic Streptomycin was developed from cultures of earth fungi. It would appear that the emanations from the damp soil in Arakan contained Streptomycin and so at this time, I was having allergic reactions to an antibiotic which had not then been discovered.

One day, returning with Bill Weston from a brief bird-watching stroll to the banks of the Naf estuary, I found the movement order for No 7 awaiting me. To cover casualties from an attack in the Tunnel area, we were to move to Yangataung. The Unit was on its way shortly after breakfast and before noon settled in the new location. Although, once again, there were sounds of considerable activity near the Tunnels, large numbers of wounded did not materialise. Within a few days we received a visit from Brigadier Meneces who confirmed the rumour that No 7 could soon expect to be withdrawn for rest and re-equipping. About this time, I received the posting order that, on relief, I was to take up duties as O/C surgical division of the 125 Indian General Hospital. Meantime, No 7 Mobile Surgical Unit really was becoming mobile; no sooner were we settled in one place than there was the order to move elsewhere. Eventually, during one such move along the Maungdaw-Buthidaung road, we met up with the ADMS (Assistant Director Medical Services) (25th Division) who authorised us to return to Bawli Bazar. With the crossing of the Bawli bridge once again, the Unit completed the Arakan circular tour which had lasted just over a year.

CHAPTER FIFTEEN

Promotion

At Headquarters Bawli Bazar, a call was made on Brigadier Meneces who, over tea and biscuits, discussed future medical policy. Within the next few days, we were visited by Major Lillwall of No 12 MSU and Major Crawford of No 8 MSU; along with Willie Wilson from the CCS a miniature surgical conference was held and all the problems associated with jungle surgery were thoroughly aired. Each afternoon, the highlight of the meeting was a bathe in the muddy waters of the Pruma from off the end of the jetty; this relaxation was spoiled for Willie who, on demonstrating his expensive waterproof watch, found that it ceased to function after immersion in the *chaung*.

No 7 had joined up with No 23 CCS for accommodation and messing; for the unit there was the activity of a general sorting out and checking of equipment. Lieutenant-Colonel Virgin of the CCS was similarly engaged and I came across him bemoaning his deficiencies. Fortunately I was able to help him out and he was most grateful for the various items of equipment which I could supply from No 7's surplus. After my generous donations, I was approached by Corporal Cross who informed me that our surplus had been 'won' from that particular CCS when last we were attached to them! After the profuse expressions of gratitude by Lieutenant-Colonel Virgin, I felt that it would mar our relationship if he were given all the sordid details.

On 12th April 1944 my replacement, Major Dickinson, arrived and took over command of No 7 MSU. That evening, in the mess of No 23 CCS, there was a party at which someone presented me with an extra pip. Next morning, after completing the handover, I said farewell to the unit and travelled north by station wagon.

The author at Bawli Bazar, OC No. 7 IMSU 1943–44

Initially it came as something of a disappointment when I realised that promotion brought no more than a move to Dhuapolong just a few miles across the border from Burma. Before lunch I had presented myself to Colonel Eames, Officer Commanding the 125 IGH which was a two thousand bedded hospital housed in bamboo bashas scattered between bush covered hillocks. Here Lieutenant-Colonel Dimson, O/C Medical Division, had under his supervision the Forward Malarial Unit and, under the wing of the Surgical Division, came 600 beds allocated for venereal disease.

From the convoys arriving by road from the south, a screening of patients was required to select those needing admission and retention for further measures before they could be allowed to continue the arduous journey to base hospitals in India. In spite of all the medical memoranda, patients arrived from some units with impaired circulation because plasters had not been split; other plasters had been incorrectly applied or failed to control fractures because of improperly set plaster, suggesting that the stocks of plaster of Paris had not been kept in airtight tins. Not infrequently there were those limb injuries in which vaseline gauze had been plugged into the wounds; these patients required admission to permit adequate drainage for infection and occasionally amputation for gas gangrene.

The supervision of the VD section proved to be a headache since, in order to carry out their personal soakings, the patients tended to spread themselves on the hill sides over a wide area and often were temporarily lost by the Indian Medical Officer who was not inappropriately called Chancre Ayer. Patients with gonorrhoea under treatment with sulphonamides were liable to develop haematuria going on to anuria (suppression of urine). In the hot climate, this complication resulted from inadequate fluid intake leading to the formation of sulphonamide crystals which blocked the renal tubules.

Some patients responded to simple measures, others, like the patient we had at Tumbru, required intensive intravenous therapy and others again needed ureteric catheterisation through a cystoscope before the flow of urine could be re-established. Later, I heard that on the Imphal front such patients with anuria invariably cleared during the rough jeep journey down from the mountains to base hospital; one surgeon developed a new technique in which he cleared the crystal blockage by rocking his anuric patients over a barrel!

Incidents were not infrequent on the routine inspections of the VD section. The British patients tended to be more militant, no doubt resenting their retention in a forward hospital. On one round, finding the syphylis ward littered with cigarette packets, fag ends, pieces of pineapple and banana skins, the inmates were told to clean up the *basha* and if their cleaning was not satisfactory, cigarettes would be stopped. Their barrack room lawyer insisted that legally an officer had not the authority to ban cigarettes which were an army issue. They had no answer when, in return, it was pointed out that a medical officer, if he considered it a necessary part of their treatment, could forbid smoking; on the next visit, the ward was clean and tidy.

On another occasion, an unknown Indian medical officer attached himself to the round of inspection; on enquiry as to who and what he was, he stated that he belonged to the Forward Malarial Unit but he was now a patient. On further questioning as to the location of his ward, he pointed to a *basha* on the top of the hill;

'But that is the syphylis ward!'

'Oh yes, sir. I'm being treated there for a sore on the genital organ.'

Truly a pox doctor!

From the VD section, regular lists of circumcisions had to be carried out; one morning, before such a list, Major Jimmy Morton remarked that he was tired of giving anaesthetics and he had always wished that he had specialised in surgery which he considered would have given him a greater insterest. I suggested that for the morning we could change places; I gave the anaesthetics and he most adequately carried out the circumcisions to clear away stinking ulcerated foreskins; thereafter he more contentedly settled back to his proper role.

Many routine sigmoidoscopies were required for patients in the dysentery section of the hospital and I well remember one such patient, an Indian medical officer, who was convinced that the introduction of the metal viewing tube through the anus was a major surgical procedure. He came to the theatre insisting that he should be given a general anaesthetic; it was pointed out to him that a general anaesthetic was best avoided for this minor examination and he was shown that the calibre of the instrument was less than that of the proctoscope which he had tolerated without complaint. Still loudly protesting, he was assisted on to the portable operating table and coaxed into the knee-elbow position. No sooner had the sigmoidoscope been passed through the anus than he began shouting and jumping about to such an extent that the operating table collapsed; we both landed in a heap on the floor and the end of the table swung round to crack him on the head. Fortunately, neither he, nor I, nor the sigmoidoscope sustained any damage. The table was re-assembled and without another word he calmly submitted himself to the examination. Afterwards, I often wondered whether or not he thought that I had hit him on the head with the sigmoidoscope to beat him into submission.

At the 125, surgical clinics were held once a week for out-patients from surrounding units; the medical officers would indicate the nature of the complaint and the appointment would be given. At one such morning session, a patient with suspected haemorrhoids had failed to put in an appearance. I was on the point of leaving the out-patient *basha* when a figure, waving a chit, was seen hurrying towards me across the dusty compound. In my imperfect Urdu I told off the sepoy for being late and without further ado, he was hustled into the consulting room with the order '*Pantaloon kolo*' (remove your trousers).

With a little hesitation, he complied with the order and meekly submitted to a full rectal examination. Having found no sign of haemorrhoids, I then read the note which I had assumed was from the man's medical officer. It came as something of a surprise to find that the message was from Colonel Eames who wished to have me call at his office. Before complying with the O/C's request, I was able to get hold of an interpreter who spoke the messenger's dialect and through him gave my explanation and apology.

Natives from surrounding villages not infrequently presented themselves with various chronic surgical conditions such as jungle sores and leg ulcers. In some instances in-patient treatment was indicated and this was possible during quiescent periods after light convoys resulted in ample vacant beds. With several days of concentrated local measures, the ulcers could be cleaned up and be ready for skin grafting to complete the process of healing. Circles of whole skin, a tenth of an inch in diameter would be taken from the skin of the abdominal wall and placed as a mosaic over the raw area; after five days of immobilisation, the pinch grafts usually had taken and thereafter the islands would spread out to give a complete covering of skin. I usually took the grafts to leave a pattern of my initials on the donor area; there may still be a few Arakanese who proudly display their abdomens carrying the mark of J. A. B.

As at this time No 7 Mobile Surgical Unit was not actively engaged, it was possible for various members of the unit to pay fleeting visits to Dhuapolong. George Quayle had looked in as he passed through on his way to take up a posting in India. Corporal Cross called in company with Karem Singh who, at this stage, was seeking a recommendation for appointment as a graded surgeon. Bill Weston of No 15 MSU of necessity stayed for a few days to have his amoebic dysentery treated before being evacuated back to India. All visitors were impressed by the sight of nursing sisters who were on the strength of the hospital to provide the much needed special care.

The visits of BESA entertainment parties and various stage personalities did much to brighten life at the 125. Initially shows were staged in a bamboo theatre which was accidentally burnt out with the accompaniment of many loud bangs. On 28th April, before the construction of the new theatre had been completed, the shy twenty-four-year old sweetheart of the forces, Miss Vera Lynn, made a personal appearance; it was late on a hot afternoon that Miss Lynn, dressed in khaki slacks, gave her greatly appreciated performance from a hillside overlooking the main compound of the hospital.

From the ashes of the old theatre, there arose the 'Phoenix' which was opened by Nöel Coward who staged a remarkable one-man show with songs, recitations, jokes and messages from home. The next morning I conducted him on a tour of the surgical division and was greatly impressed by his approach to the patients who all had from him, a handshake and a kind word. He really was a most charming man.

Before I had been posted from No 7 MSU, Brigadier John Bruce, consulting surgeon of Fourteenth Army, had suggested that when I had time I should write a paper on the subject of abdominal wounds in jungle warfare. Time for this came after I had settled with the 125 IGH and in due course the paper was submitted to him. On the next occasion we met, he said that he hoped to combine my paper into a larger one he proposed to write to give an overall picture of surgery in Burma.

Months passed by and at Comilla, East Bengal, I had surgical discussions with Brigadier M. F. Nicholls who had newly arrived as consulting surgeon of SEAC (South-East Asia Command). He asked me if I knew that, in Europe, the Americans were employing a method of delayed suture for abdominal wounds. I replied that, although I had no knowledge of the American method, I had, for the greater part of my time with the mobile unit, been treating abdominal wounds in a similar manner and I had mentioned it in my paper.

He suggested that the paper be published and permission for this was given by John Bruce who had been too busy to get down to the writing of his symposium. To conform with regulations, the paper was sent to the War Office for approval and in due course General Grant returned it with his comments and the authority to publish. Once again, the paper journeyed by sea to be submitted to the *British Medical Journal.* By this time the war was over and I had been repatriated.

The editor returned the manuscript to me and in his accompanying letter stated that he did not, at this time, feel justified in publishing a paper which did not have in it the interest it would have had six months previously. The next submission was to the *British Journal of Surgery* whose editor accepted the paper but took no action about it. After several years, I received a telephone call from Sir Gordon Gordon-Taylor who asked if I could let him have some histories of cases dealt with in Burma so that he could include them in a special issue of the *BJS* on the subject of war wounds. I told him that he could make what use he liked of my paper and sent him a copy from which he selected half a dozen examples.

I then wrote to the editor of the *BJS* and suggested that he should return my paper since there seemed to be no prospect that it would ever be published. By return, I received a request that, in view of the renewed hostilities in Malaya, they would like to retain it for early publication. So, 'Abdominal wounds in jungle warfare' was published some nine years after it had been written, surely constituting an unbeatable record of delay.

Dhuapolong was situated about eight miles inland from the Bay of Bengal and at night, when the wind was coming from the west, the sound of the breakers could be distinctly heard. Occasionally it was possible to enjoy the luxury of a sea bathe when a jeep could be borrowed to negotiate the rough tracks leading to the coast. On 6th June, with Lieutenant-Colonel Sam Dimson, O/C medical division, a longer trip was made to Cox's Bazar there to liaise with No 72 IGH sited on an adjacent island to cope mainly with casualties coming back from East and West African Divisions.

As a matter of interest, we were shown several East African patients with yaws, a tropical infection not unlike syphilis, starting with skin eruptions and later involving the bones. This disease brought to mind the old chestnut about two medical students meeting in a bar. The first cleverly steered the conversation on to tropical diseases and finally mentioned the word 'Yaws'. The second student exclaimed: 'What's Yaws?', to be given the answer: 'Mine's a Scotch and soda, thank you!'

We stayed for lunch in the mess of 72 IGH and at this time there was not the slightest indication that soon afterwards the African patients would mutiny to shoot personnel and kill the commanding officer of the hospital. Back in Cox's Bazar we purchased gifts to be sent home and then hit the trail back to the 125. Whilst taking tea at a rest camp, the news came over the radio that the Allies had landed in Normandy; the opening of the second front in Europe gave a great boost to the morale of all who knew that Germany had first to be overcome before total effort could be directed against the Japanese.

Some ten days later the monsoon came in full force to flood roads and wash away bridges. Since further evacuation was halted for the time being, the surgical division had to widen its field to tackle problems in the realms of orthopaedic, eye and ENT surgery.

On July 14th 1944, I received a priority wire which read as follows:

> Restricted. A8063. Lt. Col. Baty RAMC, 125 I. G. H., selected surgeon penicillin control team 14th Army. To report to consulting surgeon, Eastern Command, en route Poona and Secunderabad.

Within 48 hours I was on my way to Cox's Bazar where it was possible to beg a lift in a Blenheim bomber bound for Comilla. On the trip north, in an effort to take my mind off the large circular opening in the floor of the body of the plane, I studied a *Reader's Digest* which provided some information about the new 'wonder drug' which now was to be available out East.

125 Indian British General Hospital at Dhuapolong

CHAPTER SIXTEEN

The Wonder Drug

After landing at Comilla, I got a truck lift to Headquarters No 1 Mess where John Bruce was waiting. He told me that my appointment as O/C 14th Army Penicillin Research Unit had been made, not because of my limited knowledge of penicillin but because after a year in the jungle, I could be expected to know as much as anyone about the special problems of the wounded from Burma. First I was required to make a trip back to India to contact Lieutenant-Colonel Hugh Harley who had just returned from Europe with all the latest information on the use of penicillin in Italy.

Because of monsoon conditions, it was uncertain when an air passage would be available. There was no alternative but to travel by train to the Brahmaputra and then board the river steamer. On this occasion, the vast river was in spate; disembarkation across a narrow plank was quite hazardous as the river bank was being rapidly eroded. Huge masses of earth, the size of a room, could be seen to break away to disappear into the yellow swirling current.

The railway tracks started at a safe distance from the bank of the widening river and after a quarter of a mile walk, I settled down for the night in the waiting train which was due to leave for Calcutta next morning at 0600 hours. An hour and a half after this time there was no sign of any activity so I, along with several others, made our way along to the engine where we found driver and fireman fast asleep in the cab. After breaking their beauty sleep, we told them to get moving; another half hour or so was required before the engine had the necessary pressure of steam to move the long train on its way towards Calcutta. Thereafter, reading and 'K' rations relieved the monotony of a slow journey to Sealdah station.

Once again no bed was available at the Grand Hotel so a chair in the lounge accommodated me for the night. Bath and breakfast were had at the Bengal Club which was again visited for lunch after a call had been paid to the School of Tropical Medicine. An air passage across India could not be obtained and I therefore left Howrah station late that afternoon on the Bombay Mail which was to be my home for the next forty-eight hours. My companion was the bacteriologist Major Goodall who also was on his way to liaise on the subject of penicillin. In Bombay, we had lunch together in the Taj Hotel and during the afternoon rested on the hotel balcony overlooking the sea. On the esplanade, after tea, entertainment was provided by a snake charmer who arranged a fight to the death between cobra and mongoose, the latter as always being the victor.

That evening, a speedy rail trip on the luxurious Deccan Queen brought me to Poona where I met up with Hugh Harley who had reserved a room for me at the Ritz Hotel. Next day there was a penicillin conference at which Hugh rattled off about the virtues of the wonder drug with which it was possible for surgeons on the Anzio beachhead in Italy, to plate femurs and completely close wounds without any infection developing. Several days were spent on visits to Poona hospitals in the company of Hugh from whom I was able to expand my knowledge on the subject. The next move was on to Secunderabad where Hugh was to establish the Base Penicillin Research Unit. Over the months that followed the establishment of our units, we regularly kept in touch to compare notes, progress and results. Once again back in the Secunderabad area where new palatial base hospitals had now been opened up, I soon met old friends with whom visits were made to the club for meals, bathing and billiards.

On my first attendance to the area headquarters at the new Allenbury Hospital, I was required to present myself to the commanding officer and made the grave mistake of not removing my revolver with belt before entering his office. After I explained that my visit was to liaise with Harley in connection with penicillin research, the Colonel glared at me through his monocle and spat out:

'What are you going to do to it? Shoot the bloody stuff?'

A few days of luxury soon passed and once again I set off on the long journey back to East Bengal. On this occasion, for some unexplained reason, all the station restaurants were closed. In the twenty-four hours spent on the Madras-Calcutta mail, some oranges and coconut milk provided the fluid; eventually it was possible to buy a loaf of bread and some jam at a wayside halt. My companion in the double-berth compartment was strangely enough another Yank major who, in civil life, worked in the film studios of Hollywood and his stories about the stars helped to relieve the tedium.

During the last afternoon, the blackening skies heralded an approaching storm which broke with all its fury and splendour as the train slowly toiled its way along the shores of Lake Chilka. By early evening we were in Calcutta where, in the Grand Hotel, I treated myself to a proper haircut and shampoo. In the barber's shop, I chatted with Squadron Leader Elverton who offered to fix me up with a seat on an east-bound plane. In exchange for the favour, I was to act as a courier for 10,000 rupees destined to pay RAF personnel in the Comilla area.

Next morning I collected the money and made my way out to Dum-Dum airport. Here I was told that the plane from Delhi would be three hours late; when eventually it did arrive, the pilot was not prepared to fly it on to Comilla. There was no alternative but to get a taxi back to the Grand where I had the money satchel deposited in the hotel safe.

Next morning, there was time to be put in so I took the opportunity to visit a photograph studio on Chowringhee to comply with a request from my wife that I should let her have a proper photograph. It was some weeks before the mounted prints caught up with me and when I saw them I was amazed to find that the 'clever' photographer had carefully touched up the negative; all sweat, whiskers and wrinkles had been removed to produce an expressionless mask which I could hardly recognise as myself!

After lunch, I returned to the airport and eventually boarded a large DC3. When the plane reached the end of the runway, there was a delay of quarter of an hour listening to the monsoon rain rattling on the fuselage like machine-gun bullets. When the full force of the storm had eased, the pilot had sufficient vision for a take off. As we flew eastwards, between gaps in the clouds, it could be seen that the main rivers had overflowed their banks and much of the Bengal delta was under water. It was still raining when we touched down but Comilla seemed to have escaped the floods. My first task was to deliver the money to the proper authority and then for the night, I found a bed at No 7 Mess.

Next morning I made my way to No 74 Indian General Hospital (Combined) situated a few miles from the centre of the town. Colonel Anderson, O/C of the hospital was first approached; fortunately he had been informed that the research unit was to be established at No 74 but it meant starting completely from scratch. There was no penicillin, no accommodation, no equipment and no personnel.

First, a long *basha* with a concrete floor, bamboo walls and a grass roof was selected near the operating theatre and adjacent to the convoy reception point. Modifications were needed to provide an enclosed room for preparation of penicillin solutions and a larger screened area was required for the dressing of wounds. Beds, appliances and equipment were soon obtained. At a meeting with the surgeons (including Vause Gregg whom I had last met in Burma), it was agreed that I should select from the convoys those wounded suitable for the particular investigation in hand at the time.

Nursing sepoys were provided by Colonel Anderson and after I had approached the PM (Principal Matron), Sisters Dobbin and Evans arrived. Later Sister Holroyd was put in charge of the nursing staff. Colonel Pat Sayers, consultant in pathology, was particularly helpful in arranging for the necessary bacteriology. Initially Major Goodall was available until early October 44 and then he was replaced by Major John Ives who brought with him a mobile laboratory truck in which it was possible to check penicillin blood levels and carry out sensitivity tests on the bacteria obtained from wounds. In due course general duties officer Captain Joan Ball arrived to give assistance with the care of patients and the keeping of records. At first penicillin was in short supply but eventually regular consignments reached us after having been flown direct from America where the antibiotic was being manufactured on a large scale.

The type of admission to the research ward depended entirely upon the nature of the injury and not upon the race, colour or rank of the patient. In addition to having a supply of either chest wounds, gun-shot wounds of femur or nerve injuries for the research requested by higher authority, it was possible to maintain a selection of general injuries for demonstration to visiting surgeons. A month after being established, regular three-day courses of instruction were commenced to show the uses and limitations of penicillin.

From the steady stream of surgeons who came from forward hospitals, casualty clearing stations and mobile surgical units, I was able to greet old friends and make new ones. Willie Wilson gave me all the news on the activities of No 7 MSU which, at the time of his visit, was stationed on the Teknaf Peninsula.

During his short stay at Comilla, Willie restarted a dice school.

On the penicillin instruction courses, a lecture had to be given followed by a detailed ward round and operation list for demonstration. Although officially not part of the course, it was usual for the evening to be rounded off with drinks and the visitors were then given the opportunity of losing a few rupees at liar dice.

On occasions, problems cropped up in the multi-racial ward, particularly from the Africans who regarded themselves as being superior to the Indians. This outlook was demonstrated by an incident which occurred near the hospital. An African had wandered into an Indian village and raped the head-man's wife. For protesting, the headman had his hands cut off and the village was set on fire. Then the villagers really set about the intruder and gave him a thorough beating to produce multiple injuries for which admission was required. The patient not only moaned about his wounds but let it be known that he was deeply hurt that the natives should have, in such a way, treated a soldier who had come all the way from Africa to defend them against the Japanese!

Many of the West Africans, on recruitment, favoured the name 'Banana' so, in order to avoid confusion, the recruiting officer gave them colourful new names. I had my attention drawn to one record card sporting the name 'Clever Bugger'! They spoke and understood a type of pidgin English; at first it seemed strange to hear a prim ward sister, instead of enquiring whether or not the patient had moved his bowels, come out with the basic phrase – 'Have you shit good?'

A member of the 'Banana' family came to us with a through and through bullet wound of the elbow. X-ray showed that the joint was completely disorganised, no fragment being larger than the size of a pea; truly a bag of bones. The wounds of the soft tissues were excised, penicillin therapy was given and the arm was encased in plaster to hold the elbow at the optimum angle for the expected ankylosis (growing together of bones). No infection developed and in due course the plaster was removed in the hopes that a satisfactory fusion had occurred. The next morning I was greeted by a joyous Banana waving his arm freely with full movement at the elbow joint.

The East Africans were tall in stature and had good physiques. They had their cheeks scarred with tribal markings, the incisor teeth were filed to points and their ear lobes had been opened up to take an ornament a couple of inches in diameter; in the ward, this ear lobe loop was worn slung over the top of the ear. One such East African named Otteli reached the ward in a poor condition because of an infected right upper chest wound through which the great vessels from the heart could be seen pulsating. Suction drainage of the lower chest was instituted and the wound had an occlusive dressing applied. Since the infecting organisms were sensitive to penicillin, large doses were given. As his appetite improved, Otteli was demanding lion's blood and milk; we did our best to satisfy him with a cocktail of cow's blood and milk. He also fancied Brylcream sandwiches which presented no supply problem. Gradually his general health improved, the chest opening closed over and the lung re-expanded.

I had intended delaying his further evacuation for a week by which time it was expected that healing would be complete. Early one morning I received an urgent call to the ward which was in turmoil. Otteli who was by now freely ambulant, had taken a violent dislike to Harold, the Indian night orderly. With a long treacherous-looking knife, the African had first stalked and then chased Harold who sought refuge by locking himself in the penicillin preparation room. Eventually I persuaded Otteli to return to his bed and Harold was rescued to be sent off duty. Later that day, Otteli was on the convoy leaving Comilla and I marked him on my records as 'cured'.

Near Comilla was a string of forward hospitals used to accommodate wounded from the Arakan, the Imphal and the Central fronts. A delay at this junction in the lines of communication was needed before further evacuation over hundreds of miles to the base hospitals in India. Anyone coming to East Bengal invariably landed in Comilla to make a tour of the hospitals. Between operating, teaching, keeping detailed records and making reports, it made a pleasant change to conduct visitors round the Research Unit.

John Bruce frequently appeared and once brought with him Brigadier Naunton Morgan whose ward round lasted a couple of hours. Later an entertaining evening was spent at the club where over dinner, John Bruce's Scottish anecdotes were capped by long involved Welsh stories from Naunton Morgan. An inspection by Brigadier Bridgeman was followed by a group of Indian Government officials and then a general arrived to demand a special instruction course compressed into an hour. Sir William and Lady Slim called and the next week it was the turn of Lady Louis Mountbatten.

Famous stage personalities gave shows in the Garrison theatre and often found time to put on a special performance for our bedridden patients. The superb Marie Burke was followed by her glamorous daughter Patricia. Edith Evans after a magnificent performance in *The Late Christopher Bean* looked in and whilst sitting in the duty room over a cup of tea, had a wandering hen hop on her lap and lay an egg.

In the mess after the Semon, Forsyth and Farrel show, the radiologist tried to persuade the lady contortionist to let him X-ray her spine and hips but she refused. Joyce Grenfell gave a selection of her songs, recitations and impersonations which were greatly appreciated by the British patients. As we walked over to the mess, I was chatting with her lady pianist who told me that she came from Lincolnshire and in the ward had talked with a soldier coming from the same county. She remembered that he was a sergeant with a buttock wound and I realised that he was the man on whom, a few days previously, I had had to carry out an extensive excision for muscle infected with gas gangrene.

On the ward round next morning, I made a point of having a word with Sergeant Priestly and asked him where he lived in Lincolnshire. When he told me Horncastle, I said that that town was not far from Market Rasen where I was born. Then Priestly said:

'Sir. What is your name?'

'Baty.'

'Not Jackie Baty?'

'Yes.'

'Surely you remember me – little Donny Priestly – we used to play football together in Market Rasen!'

I had to admit that his memory was accurate but he could not blame me for not recognising him: he was no longer a curly-headed boy in short pants but a somewhat bald grown-up man. Thanks to penicillin, Don made a good recovery and was evacuated back to India. Some months later, from the UK, I received a cutting from a local newspaper; there was a full paragraph giving a somewhat distorted account of the event. The heading of the news item read: 'Drama in the operating theatre. Long lost friends meet again.'

In addition to the routine work required for a great variety of war wounds, penicillin was tried out on half a dozen cases of tetanus (mentioned in a previous chapter) and for a single patient with anthrax. I believe that this was the first time that the antibiotic was used for the treatment of this highly lethal infection. An Indian who worked with a mule company was admitted to the isolation ward; he was extremely ill with toxaemia (blood poisoning), ran a high temperature and on his forehead was a grossly swollen pustular area with black scabs in the centre. From this area, our bacteriologist was able to isolate the anthrax bacillus. Since the germ was sensitive to penicillin, initially large doses were given by injection but the patient's condition continued to deteriorate. After forty-eight hours, using swabs soaked in penicillin solution, we started with frequent local applications to the raw forehead and then the fever quickly subsided, the ulcerated forehead became clean and soon healed to be followed by complete recovery.

14th Army Penicillin Research Unit, 1945

The explanation was that at first the anthrax bacillus was not being reached by penicillin injections. The bacillus tends to remain and multiply at the site of skin penetration where it produces the potent poisons which are absorbed into the general circulation. It was only when the local factory of toxin production was directly attacked that the disease was controlled.

From the northern front, the medical divisions in the Comilla area were often flooded with patients suffering from scrub typhus. The condition was not helped by penicillin and my only contact with the disease was when I was asked to see soldiers with both war wounds and typhus. An incident connected with this disease arose at No 74 IGH. From a large convoy of typhus cases, two soldiers were pronounced dead and were put on ice in the mortuary *basha*. During the early hours of the morning, screams coming from the mortuary brought the guards rushing to open the door and liberate a frantic man who, thanks to the ice, had recovered consciousness and suddenly realised that he was sharing a bench with a corpse. Next day there was a court of enquiry and *bahut taklif* (much trouble) for the medical officers responsible.

In our penicillin research we needed to find out the best balance between dosage and frequency of injections. To obtain this information, Major John Ives, in his mobile laboratory truck carried out a series of blood level estimations. From the VD section of the hospital, 'volunteers' with acute gonorrhoea were detailed to attend; 12,500 units of penicillin were injected and followed over a few hours by taking half-hourly blood samples. The results of the tests were useful to us and even more useful to the patients whose gonorrhoea was cleared by the single injection.

At one time there were doubts about the advisability of issuing penicillin to forward units since it was considered that, if not kept in a refrigerator, the antibiotic lost its potency. John Ives showed that this was so once the solution had been made up but penicillin powder in an unopened ampoule kept in the sun was still effective after a month. The most important outcome of our work was confirmed by Hugh Harley at base hospital Secunderabad. We both concluded that out East, because of the high incidence of penicillin-resistant germs, primary suture of war wounds was undesirable.

As a postscript to penicillin research, I feel that it would be worth mentioning that soon after the establishment of the unit, I had a demand from a senior matron that I should supply penicillin and arrange for the ward sisters to give two-hourly injections of it to her cat. The animal had developed snuffles, cough and nasal discharge; I explained that the infection was likely to be a form of cat flu caused by a virus which would not be penicillin sensitive. In spite of this she insisted that the treatment should be given. This raised a ticklish point as, at the time, penicillin was in short supply but this matron was the 'girl friend' of a general who might make difficulties if the demand were refused.

As a compromise, I collected the dregs from the penicillin bottles enough to give a yellow solution and then added a small dose of morphia which, in cats, produces excitement rather than sedation. After the first injection, she was on the phone to tell me that no more injections must be given, penicillin did not suit her cat which had become violent and gone up the wall. So she was satisfied that I had co-operated, I was satisfied that time and penicillin had not been wasted and the cat was satisfied because it recovered without a series of painful injections.

CHAPTER SEVENTEEN

Pastoral Visits

Following his take-over, Major Dickinson had settled in with No 7 at Bawli Bazar and after several quiet weeks, George Quayle was replaced as anaesthetist by Yorkshireman Captain P. W. Hopper. The remainder of the unit was unchanged and in due course migrated to the Teknaf Peninsula to set up in tents. There was no call for any surgery and the only activity came from the Mustang fighters making daily raids across the Naf until the onset of the monsoon. Having re-equipped and rested for the period of the rains, No 7 once again moved forward to Bawli Bazar and then over the pass to Goppe Bazar. Here attention was required for a limited number of casualties resulting from the southern push on the east of the Mayo Ridge. Apart from a stand-to in readiness for a Jap counter attack which did not materialise, there was little to relieve the boredom at this time. In the ample spare time, theatre orderly Shrider was taught to drive a 15 cwt truck which had been acquired as an extra vehicle from ordnance depot in exchange for six bottles of Solan beer.

In October 1944, Major Willie Wilson took over the unit which moved back to Teknaf and settled near the shore on the west side of the peninsula where later I paid them a visit. Here there was considerable military activity as preparations were under way for sea-borne landings in hops along the coast to Akyab and Ramree Island. By February 1945 No 7 was working with a field ambulance on Ramree and in May, after Major Wilson had been invalided back to India, the unit was withdrawn to Chittagong to join XV Corps. In July No 7 was flown across the Chin Hills to Meiktila to cover the advance of the Twelfth Army down Burma.

The first atomic bomb had been dropped on Hiroshima on 6th

August, the second bomb fell on Nagasaki on 9th August and the Japanese surrendered on 12th August. At this time No 7 finished its active career at Hmawbi, on the Prome road, about ten miles north of Rangoon. In its travels the unit had sampled most forms of transport. Initially there had been the rail journey to Chittagong followed by the sea trip to Maungdaw. Then, apart from one move by river steamer, came trucking for well over a year. The mule, the landing craft and the Dakota aircraft were all tried before No 7 reached the end of the road in its own trucks.

When preparing the story of No 7 MSU, I wrote to the Historical Section at New Delhi requesting a list of officers, records of places and movement dates. It was disappointing to receive a tatty document with mispelt names and places. From my own knowledge of the unit, I realised that the supplied information was grossly inaccurate. Delhi admitted that from December 44 onwards no records were available except that No 7 Indian Mobile Surgical Unit was finally disbanded in Poona on 14th March 1947. It is difficult to imagine what the unit was doing for nearly two years after the cessation of hostilities.

From Comilla at intervals, I was called upon to make visits to outlying hospitals, to casualty clearing stations and to mobile surgical units, the latter having multiplied considerably during the previous year. Such trips made a welcome change from routine work at the Penicillin Centre and they enabled contacts to be made with many old friends, particularly in forward areas. The last time I saw No 7 MSU was early in December 1944. Prior to this Willie Wilson had attended on one of the penicillin instruction courses and then he suggested that a trip to see my old unit would be welcomed at any time.

A month after his visit, when I was feeling vaguely off-colour and in need of a change, I thought that this would be a good opportunity to avail myself of his invitation. At the Comilla club, I met a friendly pilot who offered to fly me down to Teknaf in a light plane which could land on the sandy beach. When I mentioned this proposal to John Bruce, he told me that Teknaf was a closed area as preparations were being made for the assault on Akyab. He considered that it would be risky to make such an unofficial trip in a light plane.

Major Willie Wilson, OC No. 7 IMSU, 1944–45

Personnel of No. 7 IMSU in 1945

As an alternative, he suggested that I should accompany him on his tour of inspection to the south and when required I could give talks on penicillin at the various places visited. So we set off by Dakota to call first at Chittagong and then Cox's Bazar; a truck next took us on to Dhuapolong still the home of 125 IGH. Here, from the stage of the Phoenix theatre, I delivered the lecture which stimulated the usual questions as to the effectiveness of penicillin in chronic gonorrhoea.

The next day, we continued our journey south, leaving the dusty roads and driving down the firm sand beach of the Bay of Bengal, to find No 7 in tents beside the shore. After a sea bathe and a re-union party, the night was rounded off with a poker dice session. The bathe might not have been so enjoyable had it been known what lurked in the beach. The night hundreds of large crabs with prominent luminous eyes and fearful-looking claws, left the sea and crawled well above the high-water mark. They stopped just short of our tents and by dawn were back in the sea once again.

At Teknaf, I noticed that Willie Wilson was sweating much more profusely than usual but he made no complaint, he had not lost weight and he was as energetic and cheerful as ever. On all sides there was evidence of intense military preparation and Commando units were getting ready for action, playfully tossing grenades around amongst themselves. The RAF dominated the skies and quickly dealt with any enemy plane foolish enough to approach the area. Dog fights on high provided a diversion whilst just outside a tent, I sat in a dentist's chair having tooth filling carried out.

After a couple of enjoyable days at this restful seaside resort, I had to return to Comilla and, on my own, driving a station wagon, set off northwards on the beach. As I sped along the sands, some Hurricane pilot on patrol decided to take a closer look at the solitary vehicle. The first indication of this attention was the flash ahead of a fighter plane which had passed a few feet above the car and then came the shock from the roar of its engine. This unexpected visit from the blue had a detrimental effect upon my steering and there was considerable lurching and swaying before the car could be brought to a halt. After a few minutes stop to regain my equilibrium and to light a pipe of Coolie Cut, I continued my journey without further incident.

The author when visiting Major Willie Wilson at Teknaf

For some unexplained reason, at Dhuapolong, I got involved in a medical policy conference at which Brigadier Meneces put us in the picture on the plans for the invasion of Akyab. It was proposed that, after a naval bombardment, the Commando units were to launch the attack and as soon as possible after this, No 7 Mobile Unit was to establish itself in the ruins of the town hall to carry out the initial surgery. I have no recollection of volunteering, but it was considered to be a good idea that I should attend the invasion as a surgical observer. After going in with the invading forces, I was to report on how the medical units managed to cope and then I would be required to liaise between No 7 and the off-shore ships to supervise the transference of casualties. For this exercise, it would be necessary for me to join the invading force back in India and the date of the attack was fixed for 9th January 1945. Maybe the Japanese got word that No 7 MSU was to join the assault for they evacuated Akyab on 5th January, without a shot being fired!

A month later, I was asked by Lieutenant-Colonel Andy Lutton, O/C surgical division of the 79 IGH to pay a visit to Agartala which was some fifty miles from Comilla. He supplied driver and truck and we left Comilla at sundown. Our destination was reached four hours later. At intervals along the lonely bumpy road, temporary halts were required whilst various livestock, including elephant and water buffalo slowly ambled across in front of our headlights.

The next day, still feeling saddle sore, I toured No 79 and No 51 IGH and after ward rounds gave my usual lecture on penicillin. Adjacent to the hospitals, an empty unfurnished Maharajah's palace afforded me more than adequate accommodation for the night. In order to avoid a tedious truck journey back to my unit, it was suggested that I might seek an airlift from the nearby aircraft repairs depot. On presenting myself here, I sought out the officer in charge who directed me to join Squadron Leader Touch who was due to take a recently serviced Dakota on a test flight to Comilla. In the cockpit he was demonstrating the controls to a pilot who previously had not flown this type of aircraft but Touch assured me that he would only let the newcomer take over for their flight back to Agartala. Shortly after becoming airborne, there was a loud nerve-shattering crash as one of the engines parted with its cowling but neither pilot seemed to notice this incident. Soon we were flying south at 5,000 feet in a narrow belt of cloud and I enquired:

'Why are you flying blind when at a few hundred feet higher we would be above cloud or if we dropped a little lower, the ground would be visible?'

'I like flying in cloud. It makes a change!'

'There is a fair amount of air traffic between Comilla and Agartala, suppose we meet a plane coming in the opposite direction?'

'Oh then I guess we've had it!'

After landing, we had a drink in the canteen; Touch and his pupil then re-boarded the plane and the 'L' pilot took the controls. The machine sped along the runway, rose a few feet from the ground and then bumped its wheels back on the tar-mac to continue its run. As the plane hurtled towards the palm trees at the end, it seemed that a crash was inevitable but at the last moment, on full throttle, the Dakota suddenly swept up into the sky. I feel sure that the squadron leader had suddenly realised that it was high time he took over.

It was suggested, a few weeks later, that I should visit medical units on Burma's northern front and provisional arrangements were made for me to get a lift across on the 'meat' plane which left Comilla each day. After lunch I settled on board and made a comfortable seat on one of the packing cases with which the plane was loaded. Casually I enquired as to what the case contained and was told 'grenades'. It appeared that this was the 'ammunition plane'; the 'meat plane' had left an hour earlier. There was no alternative but to sit it out. We crossed the Chin Hills carpeted with thick dark jungle out of which protruded mountain peaks reaching up to 10,000 feet.

Eventually south of Mandalay, the wide Irrawaddy came into view and we circled low over Pagan, the ancient city of a thousand white pagodas, to land on a minute air strip west of the river. Wreckages of planes were strewn along the sides of the narrow runway and just beyond the end of the strip was the smouldering remains of the 'meat plane'!

At the No 19 CCS I met up with John Bruce and with him next

morning, visited No 14 CCS before going on to a mobile surgical unit getting ready for the push towards the south. Because of the approaching monsoon, flights across the Chin Hills were less frequent but I managed to get a place on the last plane bound for Comilla. In the short time since my flight to the east, a huge mass of dense cloud had built up completely obscuring the mountains. The Dakota, carrying a few wounded, circled higher and higher in an effort to get above the pink tinged clouds but having reached its ceiling about 15,000 feet it turned westwards into and through the formidable barrier. There was an opening about half the size of a door in the fuselage on one side; through it we had a close up view of the constant discharges of lightning and those of us wearing light battle-dress were soon feeling the cold.

The plane must have been well built to stand the buffeting it received as it suddenly dropped or rose hundreds of feet. At times it seemed to be moving sideways like a crab and even the pilot looked worried. All the wounded soon required attention for the effects of the cold and vomiting. As I had clear vision of the underlying terrain on the outward journey, it did not add to my peace of mind to think about what lay below. At dusk we all were relieved to land safely at Comilla which at the time was experiencing one of its worst thunderstorms. On reaching the hospital, I found that my bamboo *basha* had caved in and the surrounding banana trees had been flattened. I managed to crawl inside the ruins to spend the night in my camp bed which was still dry and intact.

Apart from the odd few days off for a surgical conference in Calcutta, I had been with No 7 in Burma, without a break, for over a year. After leaving Arakan, applications for leave were granted and provisional arrangements were made. Then there would come a posting or for some other reason the leave would be cancelled and the process of application had to be started once again. Eventually in May 1945, I got my one and only leave for a fortnight which was to be spent in the company of Bill Weston at Kodaikanal, South India.

We had met at the Grand Hotel, Calcutta and on visiting the RTO (rail traffic officer) had been informed that there was no vacancy on the Madras Mail for at least a week. Bill was most

The author and Major Bill Weston on leave at Kodaikanal

indignant at the prospect of spending half the leave in a hot steamy city and suggested that we should try our luck at Howrah station. On the platform, he disappeared into the dense crowd to return in a few minutes with the news that we had been found a place on the mail train. It seems that he had chatted up the Indian guard who, after a tip (or bribe) of 20 rupees, had allocated us a double compartment complete with ice boxes.

The guard must have considered that he had been overpaid because, before the train drew out, he sought out Bill Weston and suggested that, if so desired, Bill could for the night, have the company of a very nice Madrassi lady. The offer was declined with thanks.

During the journey, which took just over a couple of days, we joined up with a drinking and dice party run by some combatant officers. Although my memory of the sessions in their compartment is rather vague, I do recall that one of the officers was a Czeck called Bata. He told me that in civilian life he owned a shoe manufacturing business; at that time, I did not realise that his name was known throughout the world and in 1938 when Hitler had invaded Czeck territory, Bata's factory had been taken over.

At Madras, with severe hangovers, we changed stations to catch the Trivandrum express on the narrow gauge line and after an hour reached Kodaikanal Road. Then there was the bus journey from the red arid plain winding to some seven thousand feet above sea level to cool Kodaikanal. Here we were welcomed by Bill's relative, the Reverend Arthur Rumpus whose hospitality we enjoyed for the duration of the leave. Each morning, Bill's premature start on breakfast had to be halted to allow the saying of Grace and at the end of meals there were prayers together with the reading of a passage from the Bible.

Our stay with the missionary provided a most pleasant change. In addition to the visit to Lake Perriare where we found the leech-infested forest (previously mentioned in Chapter 6), there were unsuccessful hunts for wild boar, Kodi lake provided boating and bathing facilities, the mountain slopes afforded sights of ibex and in the local colourful market there were excellent furs to be bought at bargain prices.

Whilst on leave, I received a letter from John Bruce who gave me the news that, during the push towards Rangoon, Willie Wilson had become seriously ill with high fever. His sputum had been found to be positive for TB and every effort was being made for him to be evacuated from Burma by hospital ship. In June, I heard from Willie himself after he had reached the 126 IBGH in Poona where his chest condition was responding to treatment. The foundation member of the Arakan poker dice school concluded his letter:

'The play whilst it lasted was great fun and I've no regrets. You can't win 'em all against loaded dice.'

CHAPTER EIGHTEEN

Towards the Setting Sun

By the end of June 1945, refreshed from the leave in Kodaikanal, once again I was back in Comilla to continue the work at the research unit for another month. Colonel Anderson, O/C of 74 IGH, had been replaced by Colonel Jim Dryberg who gave me the news that I had been awarded the OBE and he insisted on having a celebration party at which he pinned the salmon-pink ribbon on my bush shirt.

Shortly before I left Comilla, an unfortunate incident arose on the surgical side of one of the local hospitals. A British medical officer prescribed and gave the incorrect dose of a drug resulting in the death of the patient. The offending officer was promptly arrested and put under armed guard. John Bruce approached the general to request that the man be freed from close arrest as no criminal offence had been committed. He would in due course be brought before a court of enquiry whose members were medical men qualified to understand this particular problem in which there had been a genuine mistake. The general was loth to agree.

John then pointed out that if any high-ranking combatant officer made an error of judgement such as happened at Donbaik when many hundreds of lives were sacrificed, that commander did not find himself under close arrest. The general reacted violently to this remark which he said should never have been made to him by a mere brigadier and must never again be mentioned. When however tempers had cooled, the medical officer was released from custody to await the court of enquiry.

Now that the war in Europe was over, increasing activity was directed towards the Japanese. The combatant forces, supported by the mobile units and casualty clearing stations, were either island hopping along the coast or pushing southwards beside the Irrawaddy towards Rangoon. Early in July, I had a call to attend at ALFSEA headquarters to see Brigadier Nicholls. After the now familiar journey across the Brahmaputra, I boarded the Calcutta train and got off at Barrackpore, a few halts short of the terminus. At HQ, Old Nick (as Brigadier Nicholls was known) went over the records and discussed problems, particularly those connected with mobile surgical units. Since the Akyab mission had not materialised, he suggested that in due course, I should accompany the proposed attack on Port Swettenham in Malaya some 250 miles north of Singapore. After the barrage from the fleet had, in theory, flattened the defences, I was to go in with the assault forces to act as surgical observer and adviser until the mobile units were established and working. He said he would get in touch with me when the actual date of this invasion had been finally settled. In the meantime, I was to re-visit Secunderabad to liaise with Hugh Harley at the Base Penicillin Research Unit. In order that I should have something to fill in the spare time, he supplied me with a thick pile of mobile unit and CCS records. From these I was required to make an analysis of all deaths resulting from abdominal wounds and in due course let him have my report with comments.

In Calcutta, I managed to get a bed in the Grand Hotel and next day, on Chowringhee, I literally bumped into Major Jim Morton who, some eighteen months previously, had been my anaesthetist at the 125 IGH in Arakan. Jim's repatriation order had just come through; his celebrations had got him into such a confused state that he did not know whether he was coming or going but, in his more lucid intervals, he insisted that he must be on the Bombay Mail that evening. I coaxed him back into the Grand Hotel, plied him with coffee and sorted out his papers and travel warrants. A few hours later when he was more sober but still very shaky, I took him by taxi to Howrah station. There I put him on the correct train and managed to find another repatriate officer who promised to look after Jim until he had completely recovered from the alcoholic anaesthetic.

Before getting on my way to the Deccan, I had first to return to No 74 IGH, to complete the winding up of the Penicillin Unit. On 18th July, I said farewell to Comilla and soon was back on the steamer which on this occasion, was held up at Golanda Ghat for four hours before it was considered safe to let passengers disembark. In the couple of weeks since I had last been at Golanda, the western bank had been eroded by another hundred yards and as it was still crumbling at the landing point, the gangway between steamer and shore was by no means stable. Once on dry land, I watched with trepidation as a coolie carrying my tin trunk on his head, bounced across a swinging plank to deposit all my possessions at a safe distance from the fast flowing Brahmaputra. On arrival at Sealda Station, Calcutta, in the early hours of the Thursday, I took my luggage across to Howrah Station and there booked a seat on the Bombay Mail due to leave that evening. The train journey across the Central Plain of India was uninspiring and most aptly fitted the description given to it by the British soldier: 'Miles and miles of bugger-all and cows eating it!'

Victoria Station, Bombay was reached late on the Saturday afternoon and I had to stay at the Taj Hotel for a couple of nights before an onward booking could be obtained. Opportunity was taken to wander the crowded colourful streets of the city, to stroll along the sea front and to inspect 'the Gateway to India', that monument built by the British Raj. My main memory of the Taj Hotel was of there enjoying the luxury of a prolonged soak in a full-sized porcelain bath.

On the way to the Deccan, I broke my journey at Poona to visit Willie Wilson at the 126 IBGH. It came as quite a shock to see the change in my friend who, although still as cheerful as ever, was no more than a shell of his former self. He told me that since his last letter to me a couple of months previously, there had been a marked improvement in his general condition. His fever had settled, his cough was less troublesome and he had managed to put on a little weight. It was expected that within the next fortnight, he would be fit for evacuation home, a short stay being made en route in South Africa. Before we parted company, he gave me his original set of ivory dice which had seen so much action in Arakan.

Back in Secunderabad once again, I shared a bungalow with Hugh Harley, O/C of the Base Penicillin Research Unit. Here attention had been given to the methods of administering penicillin and to the treatment of infected wounds involving bone. Major Terry Bowie concentrated on bacteriological investigations which confirmed the findings of Major John Ives at Comilla. In the light of this, we started on the production of a combined paper entitled 'The pathogenicity of penicillin-resistant infection' which, after the War, was eventually published in *The Lancet*.

Visits to the specialised hospitals in the area started a friendship with Major Eric Peet, the plastic surgeon, and with Major Sandy Slessor, whose main task was the repair of nerve injuries. On the advice of Sandy, the mobile surgical units were told not to put a black stitch marker into the divided nerve ends as this increased scarring up the nerve. At the Penicillin Research Unit, I had been told to carry out a series of nerve sutures a few days after injury and I confirmed Sandy's opinion that, even with penicillin, early repair of nerves was not to be recommended; it was best to delay operation for at least six weeks.

Eric Peet, as well as being master in his speciality, was a talented landscape painter, a big game hunter and a true craftsman in the art of making violins. In a bungalow he shared with Sandy, Eric kept a pet leopard which sometimes caused alarm to visiting guests, especially if they happened, on awakening, to find it asleep under the bed. When exercising his pet, Eric always took the precaution of wearing thick gauntlets. Outdoors, the leopard would dash at full speed towards his master, swerve at the last moment to give him a tap with its sheathed paw as it flashed past and then turn to repeat the process. Unfortunately the playful antics of the animal were not appreciated by the local natives who somehow managed to get it poisoned.

In addition to the plastic work required for deformities resulting from war wounds, Eric found time to give civilians the benefit of his skill at making new noses. He was always able to demonstrate some stage of the reconstruction, in which a shaped flap from the forehead was fashioned and swung down to the area of the nasal defect. The rudiments of this operation date back to ancient times and as long ago as 1794, there are descriptions of successful restorations achieved by both Italian and Hindu surgeons. Out East, for centuries, the cutting off of the nose was an accepted method of punishment. In the Deccan, the nose was frequently lost because of infidelity and this resulted in an unlimited supply of patients on whom, beds and time permitting, Eric could demonstrate his art.

In the mess of an evening, Eric and Sandy were often called upon to give their cross-talk act which would have been given an enthusiastic reception in any music hall. Sandy supplied the droll Aberdonian humour and Eric acted as stooge. They usually got round to witty remarks about Eric's bald head and the luxurious growth of hair on Sandy's nose. Seeing them at their work the next day, it was hard to appreciate that together, the previous night, they had shown themselves to be such a pair of first class comedians.

Besides visiting the various hospitals and keeping up with a full programme of social activities, each day, I set aside some hours to analyse the records supplied by Nick. I finally submitted my report in which, amongst other things, I expressed an opinion that, in mobile units, results might have been improved by the greater use of blood. In due course this suggestion produced a marked reaction from the head of the transfusion service. Not only did he disagree with my findings but he bombarded me with a string of stinging letters which continued to reach me months after my return to civilian life.

On VJ day, 15th August 1945, I joined in the widespread celebrations and also attended a wedding reception given in the Mess for Major Lawton, the former anaesthetist of No 6 Indian Mobile Surgical Unit. That day I also received the news that it would be many more months before I could expect to be repatriated. This blow was somewhat softened by the fact that my services would no longer be required at Port Swettenham. A posting order then arrived confirming my appointment as O/C surgical division of 56 IGH in Chittagong. The day before I left for East Bengal, there was time to attend the formal VJ tea party given by the Nizam of Hyderabad in his palace. No one under the rank of lieutenant-colonel received an invitation and before admission, one was required to show both invitation and identity cards. The huge decorated reception room, which opened on to the lush gardens filled with exotic flowers, was overflowing with high-ranking officers of every colour and from every branch of the services.

The Nizam, himself a strict teetotaller, did not allow any alcohol to be served and so conversation remained subdued. Neither did he permit the ladies of his harem to put in an appearance but his sons and their beautiful Persian wives circulated through the throng to chat to bemedalled brass who were balancing a cup of tea in one hand and a plate of ice-cream in the other. With several friends, I managed to get a seat at one of the few small tables and there do full justice to several helpings of special ice-cream and strawberries. In hindsight, this was probably one of the last occasions at which the Nizam was able to demonstrate his power and wealth.

After the now familiar journey to the north east, I reached Chittagong on 15th September to find that Colonel Jim Dryberg had moved from Comilla to take command of 56 IGH. This large straggling hospital was made up by a series of long wards constructed from brick, corrugated iron and bamboo. The whole complex extended for half a mile on flat ground alongside the railway line and just across the road from the hospital entrance, was the station with signal box and level crossing. On a low hill behind the hospital were bamboo *bashas* for sleeping quarters and at the foot of this hill, a large *basha* served as the officers' mess. Of an evening, sitting on the broad veranda in front of the *bashas*, one could see the glistening waters of the Bay of Bengal some eight miles away. To newcomers it was pointed out that the line of longitude E 92 which passed through Chittagong, continued south to Antarctica without touching any land, not even an island.

The shining waters of the Bay of Bengal proved less attractive at close quarters. First there was a bumpy trip in low gear along an unmade road and then little refreshment was to be found in the luke-warm sea. A long wade out was required before even the knees were covered by the mud-clouded outflow which spread across the shallows from the delta of the Brahmaputra.

As there still existed a widespread feeling of relief that the war was over, Colonel Dryberg decided that surplus mess funds should be used to give a celebration party and wholesale invitations were issued. When it was realised that the attendance would be a massive one, the fear was expressed that the supplies of alcohol might prove inadequate. The mess secretary, in collaboration with the pathologist and anaesthetist, made up a special lime cocktail laced with absolute alcohol and a touch of ether; this was offered to those guests who were eroding the supplies too quickly. It certainly had the desired effect; one drink and the visitor suddenly decided it was time he went home. Even without the cocktail, many mess members had a severe hangover next morning. One medical officer was still under the influence by late afternoon; only then was it discovered that whilst he thought that he was sipping lime juice to speed his recovery, he was in fact imbibing the special cocktail which had been accidentally supplied. It was not surprising that his misery had been unduly prolonged.

As part of the aftermath of the war, the surgical division, in addition to its routine work, was required to give attention to many Japanese prisoners. These men who had been abandoned in Burma, were admitted in an advanced state of emaciation resulting from starvation and from the effects of chronically infected wounds. They now had a very different outlook on life compared with that of their compatriots of a couple of years previously. They were no longer surly or aggressive and freely expressed profuse thanks for our efforts to restore their health. Not a single one showed any inclination to indulge in hara-kiri.

Another tidying-up exercise led to the hospital being put on 'gas alert'. We were instructed to provide facilities to cope with any mustard gas casualties. The stocks of unused mustard gas held ready in North Bengal were to be transferred to Chittagong, there to be loaded on to ships with a view to dumping the containers into the depths of the Bay of Bengal. We set about instructing personnel, recalling long-forgotten precautions and constructing decontamination centres in readiness for a possible leakage. There was the risk that a gas container, during transfer from rail to ship, might be dropped and its contents shed. Another risk was from the native population who would conclude that a guarded train probably contained something of value and their expert efforts at pilfering might have led to casualties. Fortunately, no patients needed to visit our decontamination centre.

It was of interest that, with the cessation of hostilities against the Japanese, the general attitude in the hospital underwent a gradual change, and aggression began to find its outlet in other directions. The Moslems and Hindus showed to each other an increasing aversion, which culminated in racial riots both in the hospital and in the town of Chittagong. The weapons used were mainly fists, stones and bamboo rods; no one was killed but throughout that particular night, the surgeons were kept busy patching broken heads.

At the 56 IGH many of the surgical instruments had the 'Imperial' stamp on them and as in the early days of No 7 MSU, these artery forceps, made from inferior quality metal, frequently broke, even when not in use. My application for replacements from central stores brought the reply:

'Surely you must realise that there's been a war on. New instruments are only for issue to forward units.'

Naturally this remark was not well-received; it was another example of the usual excuse for any failure to supply. I resorted to a method which in the past had proved successful. The stores were bombarded with daily messages (copies to ADMS) informing them of the number of functioning artery forceps remaining each evening and giving them the estimated date when all operating at the hospital would cease. It took a fortnight of paper work, phone calls and personal visits before new artery forceps were supplied.

When I took over the division, the surgical specialist was a handsome, popular Major who, shortly after my arrival, announced his engagement to one of the British nursing sisters. Colonel Dryberg seemed quite thrilled at the match and threw a large party to celebrate the occasion. Following the wedding and honeymoon, the major and his bride were posted in different directions. It was only after I had replaced Colonel Dryberg as acting O.C. that a stream of frantic messages came from the girl's parents asking that, at all costs, the marriage should be prevented. Her brother, an RAF pilot flew out from the UK to reinforce his parents' pleas but it was all too late. It was subsequently revealed that the major, a Moslem, already had a wife back in his home town. His religion permitted him to take as many wives as he could afford to keep. I have no knowledge as to how the affair ended, if indeed it did end. The girl may have returned to her home in England or she might have adapted herself to sharing her husband in some Pakistan town. I liked and respected Colonel Dryberg but considered that in this instance, he made an error in encouraging this mixed marriage which might have been avoided by an early posting.

The major was replaced as surgical specialist by outspoken Sam Mottershead who brought a welcome touch of Yorkshire humour to the division. In due course, he was well able to take over my surgical work when, with the departure of Colonel Dryberg, I had to give my time to administrative duties. Daily orders had to be published, disputes settled, mail attended to and punishments handed out. A complete inspection tour of the hospital was required each Friday morning and on it, I was required to taste generous samples of food in the respective Moslem and Hindu kitchens; this effectively took away any appetite for lunch and accustomed my palate to the flavour of strong curry.

The day after Colonel Jim Dryberg left, Tom Dryberg, the politician, presented himself. Although he was disappointed at just missing his older brother, he told me that he was making a tour and soon no doubt would catch up with him. He requested that he might be allowed to address as many men as possible to give them news of repatriation and messages from home. I arranged for a large recreation *basha* to be put at his disposal and filled it with convalescent patients and hospital personnel. It came as something of a surprise to hear Tom Dryberg deliver a party political broadcast in favour of the Labour Party and never mention the subject of repatriation or deliver messages from home. He painted a glowing picture of what life would be like in Britain under the new government and towards the end of his speech, talked on how the future health service would abolish all the evils of the past. At question time, he received a concentrated attack from all the doctors who drew attention to his many mistaken views and inaccuracies. As his various arguments and replies were demolished, I brought the meeting to a close. As we walked together towards the mess, he said:

'I made a really bad mistake to bring up the subject of the health service in the presence of so many medicos.'

That evening, to cheer him up, we let him win at liar dice!

On Sunday, 21st October, my repatriation order came through and the next twenty-four hours were spent in the process of handing over. I had a visit from the local ADMS who reminded me that the hospital was due, next day, to be inspected by some important general. In view of this, I was asked to delay my departure for a few days and if I agreed, then, having completed twenty-one days as acting O/C, I could put up my tabs and become a full colonel. I politely refused his offer. In hindsight I regret that I did not stay those extra few days, since it would have resulted in a considerable increase in the amount of my discharge gratuity. At the time, I was not to know that many useless days were to be wasted in Deolali and I had the fear that my postponement of 'Python' (code name for repatriation) might delay my getting home.

It was with mounting excitement that I crossed the road to Chittagong station and left behind the 56 IGH while men painted the entrance stones white in readiness for the general's inspection. Two days had to be spent in Calcutta awaiting a vacancy on the Bombay Mail. In the Grand Hotel, I met up with Captain Van Someron, whom I had known in Secunderabad, and who was due for repatriation to Kenya. We shared a two-berthed carriage and endured the weekend travelling for the last time across the central plain of India. During the journey, we busied ourselves with white paint to mark the necessary details on our tin trunks in readiness for shipment. After twenty-four hours on 'K' rations, we were ready for a square meal at Nagpur. Slow progress was then made to Basawal junction where we left the Bombay Mail and put in several hours sitting on our luggage before boarding the Deolali train.

Situated some fifty miles from Bombay, on the arid brown plain east of the Ghats, was Deolali transit camp which for decades had seen generations of British soldiers. The regular army, in addition to colouring our language with such names as 'Posh' and 'Blighty', introduced the word 'Deolali'. When used in reference to anyone, this word suggested that the individual was slightly mad or 'round the bend', a state of mind readily induced by any prolonged stay at this huge isolated camp. The single-storied, white-washed buildings were scattered over a vast acreage with not a single tree or shrub to break the monotony of the scene. The concentration camp effect was completed by the encircling close-mesh wire fence. This was not to prevent men getting out but was designed to stop rats getting in. At this time, a plague epidemic raged in the surrounding neighbourhood and the nights were illuminated by scattered fires arising from the funeral pyres of the victims. There was a constant patrol of the wire to look out for dead rats, whose fleas were the carriers of the disease.

During the three weeks I was resident in the camp, no one was allowed outside the boundary and entertainment, such as it was, had to come from inside. There were three cinemas which had a change of programme every two days so that it was possible to spend a part of each day, viewing old films from Hollywood. On one occasion, there was a riot when the GI hero, on leave after winning the war in Burma, was wooing the heroine with:

'Gee kid, we must get together. It's three months since I even saw a white woman!'

Most of the audience had not seen a white woman for over three years and the violent reaction by the troops brought this particular performance to a premature end before the place was torn to pieces.

A host of old friends and acquaintances were constantly arriving to swell the numbers in the camp. One day, Bill Weston breezed into the mess and soon was complaining about the food. His obsession over food had not been diminished either by his service in Burma or his spell as a patient with severe amoebic dysentery. A couple of years after our return to civilian life, Bill paid a weekend visit to my home in Shrewsbury and every effort was made to cater for his tastes. As we got up from the table after a very special lunch he remarked:

'I really did enjoy that meal. What time are we having dinner?'

My wife took a poor view of this and when Bill had departed said:

'If Bill Weston is a typical sample of your army friends, I don't want to see any more of them!'

Rumours constantly circulated round the camp and each morning there was a rush to the main office to find that there was no prospect of a passage home on some mythical ship. One evening, in the mess, after the usual dice session, we decided to start our own rumour to see how long it would take to become widespread. We suggested that in three days time, *Queen Mary* would come into Bombay to provide wholesale evacuation. This rumour, with certain modifications, was all round the camp within forty-eight hours. When it came back to us, it sounded so authentic that we joined the morning rush to the office to find that we had been hoisted on our own petard.

As an alternative to sea-passage home, there were readily available flights provided by the RAF but I, like many others, felt that having so far survived, we would not at this stage risk our necks. Pilots used to making bombing raids over Europe, had been put on the air-lift from India. Unfortunately many failed to cope with the special weather conditions on the route and aircraft wreckages littered the airfields between Bombay and London.

At last the great day arrived with the genuine information that passages were fixed on a number of ships docked in Bombay. My last duty in India was to act as officer in command of one of the troop trains; following military custom, everyone was on the platform in readiness, several hours before the train was due to arrive. By late morning, the slow journey across the Western Ghats had ended and once aboard SS *Cameronia*, I got my light luggage into the cabin which was to be shared with five others. The ship cast its last links with the quayside as lunch was being served but I skipped this meal to take up a position at the stern of the vessel, to watch what the British soldier considered to be the best sight in all India. I would agree that there were few more inspiring visions than that of Bombay with its Gateway of India, gradually fading into the eastern haze.

It is not likely that I will ever forget the lessons learnt in Burma. Present-day highly specialised surgeons working in modern hospitals with super-equipped operating theatres, should bear in mind that occasions do arise when it may be necessary for them to widen their field and make do without many of the facilities which at present they take for granted and regard as being essential. On the nursing side, it needs to be pointed out that adequate skills can be acquired without special qualifications, book knowledge or administrative ability. I pay tribute to both Indian and British orderlies, coming from all castes and walks of life, who, in Burma, became efficient dedicated nurses.

I still keep the old liar dice, both sets. Occasionally, I shake them out of the shabby leather cup and turn them over in my palm. After over thirty years, they still bring to mind the voices and faces of departed friends who handled them when we played for rupees in that Eastern land, where all the dice were heavily loaded against us.

Appendix

The Medical Line of Evacuation from the Arakan Front.

	Bearer Units	
Field Ambulance	Advanced Dressing Stations (A.D.S.)	
	Main Dressing Station. (M.D.S.)	Mobile Surgical Units.
	Casualty Clearing Station. (C.C.S.)	
	Forward General Hospital (I.B.G.H.)	medical. surgical Forward Malarial & V. D. Units.
	Intermediate General Hospital.	Medical, Surgical Neurosurgical Burns. Penicillin Research Faciomaxillary.
	Base Hospitals India.	Plastic Orthopaedic. Neuro-surgical. Medical, Surgical.

From bearer units to base hospitals India – One thousand miles.